C000292051

Stone a
in
Black Mountains

David Tipper

Cover picture by Michael Blackmore.

First published by David Tipper in 1975.

New Edition published by Blorenge Books in December 1985.

Reprint 1988

Reprint 1994

Copyright © David Tipper

ISBN 0 9510444 1 9

Drawings and Maps by Michael Blackmore.

Edited by Chris Barber.

Designed by Eagle Image & Design.

3, Holywell Road, Abergavenny, Gwent NP7 5LP
Tel: Abergavenny (0873) 853909.

Printed by Mid Wales Litho Limited,
Units 12 & 13 Pontyfelin Industrial Estate, New Inn, Pontypool, Gwent NP4 0DG.

CONTENTS

PREFACE

"A vexed question which arose in Monmouthshire"

The 1975 edition of this book found its way into the hands of many people previously unknown to me who played a prominent part in the Water Works construction. As a result of extensive correspondence at home and abroad much supplementary material became available. This has been incorporated with gratitude.

There was something remarkable about the long struggle to supply the rapidly developing Western valleys with adequate santitation and pure water, culminating as it did with the "Tillery" Water Board. Abertillery was the second largest town in the former county of Monmouthshire and it is surprising that this struggle, which began in 1885, could not be completed until 1928. Even more surprising was the opposition encountered from local colliery owners, the lives of whose employees depended on these amenities.

In 1910 a House of Commons' Select Committee heard the Abertillery Water Bill referred to as "a somewhat prolonged and vexed question which has arisen in Monmouthshire". It was.

Today the gigantic stone wall of the Grwyne Fawr Reservoir in the heart of the Black Mountains still compels admiration, and so it should. Let credit be given to whom credit is due.

The Grwyne Fawr Dam 1985.

4

Site of Resevoir 1913

INTRODUCTION

Ridge-walking along the Welsh Borderland hills described as the Black Mountains is a task for the 'loner'. He can walk for hours without meeting or seeing anyone. This allows time for reflective thinking. To what age does the red sandstone block belong? When the geologist answers in millions of years his reply seems to rob the present year of any significance. And what of the primitive camps or settlements? Who first lived and walked on these bare heights? There is no definite answer.

Looking down into the valley between the Gader and the Ffwddog ridges, the view includes a reservoir. Surely that should not be difficult to date. The massive retaining wall has a solid Edwardian look about it, reminiscent of the heyday of the British Empire. But why did the water have to be stored in such a remote place? Where does the pipeline go to? When was it built? And how did the contractor transport men and materials to this lonely spot in the heart of the mountains? In 1913 the late Mr. R.H. Baker-Gabb wrote a book about the Black Mountains. It was re-issued in 1918, the year of his death. In this book Mr. Gabb refers to the reservoir works under construction and also to the new approach road built by the contractor. The sharp bends and steep gradients encountered on the road certainly seem to rule out the possibility of using an alternative form of transport, or do they?

At the bottom of 'the pitch' below Partrishow Hill is a farm gate which smells of creosote. The post that supports it is a railway sleeper of unusual size. In the lane Mr. Dai Lewis was busy hedging. I asked him if there had ever been a railway line in this vicinity. "Yes" he replied "it did run up the valley to the reservoir". How odd. In 1918 Mr. Gabb said road, in 1968 Mr. Lewis said train. Who was correct? From his jacket pocket Mr. Lewis proudly produced a post card photograph depicting a sturdy little steam locomotive together with the information that his father fired it on 'the Route' to the reservoir. Such evidence was conclusive and led to the writing of this book.

'Stone and Steam in the Black Mountains' is an account of the Water Works construction carried out by the former Abertillery and District Water Board between the years 1911 and 1928. It includes a description of the Board's road and railway route into the heart of the mountains. The latter was never officially authorised because it was considered to be impossible to operate. However it had to be built and remained in use for some fifteen years. Today, few people can still remember the laying of the pipeline, the village built at Blaen-y-cwm for the work people and the train that transported men and materials to the site. It is to them that this book is dedicated.

David Tipper
Ross-on-Wye
1985

The maintenance men at Grwyne Fawr Works, period 1926. Because their work was heavy and dirty they were called the 'Black Gang'.

Grwyne Fawr Valley

Pregnant at Last

S outh-west of Hereford a long, flat line of hills cuts into the skyline and marks out the Welsh Border. Immediately beyond are the coalfields and industrial areas, heart-breaks of unemployment in the 1920s and 1930s. What did that skyline mean to "exiles" returning to their homeland? The academic might think about the Brecon Beacons, Offa's Dyke, Marcher Barons, Castles, battles fought long ago, and when it is fine the land looks lovely. But, if you had a job, life at Ebbw Vale Steelworks was hard. Was it only the Waterboard Engineer who looked at the mountains and thought about a reservoir?

The Border changed things, Hereford Railway station was 'dreamy' England, Abergavenny was not. Leaving the Cathedral city increased the sense of anticipation. There was a station called Tram Inn and another station at Pontrilas for the last English branch line to Hay-on-Wye. Then the gradients began, up through Pandy to a summit at Llanfihangel. This sounded Welsh, the scenery looked Welsh and the dash down the incline to Abergavenny was conclusive: it was Wales. Llanfihangel station became a place to remember. The locomotive exhaust compelled notice as it beat staccato, dragging the train over the foothills of the mountains visible from Hereford. The map describes them as the Black Mountains probably because the approach from the English side is usually 'into the sun' with shadow on the Herefordshire face.

In "Highways and Byways in South Wales" (1903) A.G. Bradley describes the area as *"eighty square miles of complete uncompromising solitude"* but to the hearing ear it is a noisy silence, noisy with the echoes of over a thousand years.

7

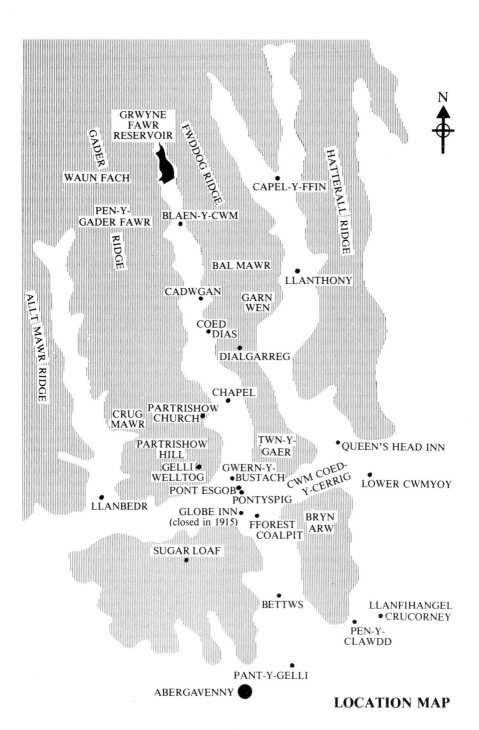

LOCATION MAP

8

The hills form a plateau varying in height from about 1500 ft. to over 2600 ft. above sea level. There are four main ridges, the Hatterrall, the Ffwddog, the Gader and the Alltmawr. Enclosed within them are the valleys of Olchon, Honddu, Grwyne Fawr, Grwyne Fechan and Rhiangoll. South-west is the river Usk, north is the river Wye and dotted around the hills are the towns of Abergavenny, Crickhowell, Talgarth, Hay-on-Wye and Longtown village. The area includes parts of Powys, Gwent and Hereford and Worcester.

It appears that the ancient glacial disturbances in the Wye Valley "broke into" the Honddu Valley and forced this stream into the river Monnow and the Wye at Monmouth. The Grwyne Valleys were only affected by local ice disturbances. They are therefore much narrower and the streams flow into the Usk at Glangrwyne. The annual rainfall is high, especially in the north-west section of the hills. The westerly air stream comes up the Towy Valley via the Col at Sennybridge to Brecon. Here it joins another air stream coming over the Beacons and both strike the Black Mountain escarpment between Talgarth and Crickhowell. This escarpment has a steep rise of over 1000 ft., the Usk and Wye Valleys are unable to drain the air away quickly enough with the resultant adiabatic cooling giving persistent and often continuous cloud and rain in winter. In the Upper Grwyne Fawr Valley the average annual rainfall is normally over 60", whereas in the south-east of the mountain area it is below 40".

The densely wooded valleys were dangerous so ancient tracks took the traveller over the mountains into central Wales. On the high ground a would-be assailant could at least be seen. The farmers working the fertile land surrounding the hills were quite remote from centres of population and from the industrial areas. This meant that commodities such as coal were expensive to obtain. The need for public transport became such a pressing one that the Brecon canal was opened early in the 19th century. In 1805 a tramroad was surveyed from the canal at Brecon to Hay-on-Wye. This was not opened until 1816, extended to Eardisley in 1818 and to Kington in 1820. In 1863/64 this horse-drawn tramroad was reconstructed as the locomotive operated Hereford Hay and Brecon Railway. The Llanfihangel Railway obtained its Act of Parliament in 1811 to build another horse tramroad 7¾ miles from the canal at Govilon to Llanfihangel village. The Grosmont Railway Act followed in 1812 and extended the line to Monmouth Cap (near Pontrilas). The former was opened in March 1814 and the latter reported complete to Llangua in March 1819. The Hereford Railway Act was passed in 1826 and in September 1829 the horse-drawn trams reached the city, via the Tram Inn. As with the Hay Railway these tramroads served as feeders to and from the canal. They were subsequently purchased by the Newport, Abergavenny and Hereford Railway and opened as a locomotive railway in 1854. The N.A. & H. Railway became a part of the West Midland Railway in 1860 and was absorbed into the Great Western Railway in 1863. This was the year in which the Brecon and Merthyr Railway came tumbling out of the Welsh mountains en route to Talybont and Brecon. The Mid Wales Railway followed suit from Llanidloes in 1864. In 1881 the little Golden Valley Railway commenced its insolvent life and official railway development in the Black Mountain area ceased. In fact the most exciting line built in the whole district penetrated into the heart of the mountains and almost to the top of them.

9

During the nineteenth century, severe cholera epidemics struck many of the South Wales industrial towns. The disease was spread through the infection of wells and springs which were the only source of water supply. In retrospect, it is no exaggeration to say that the heaviest responsibility resting on the shoulders of local government has been the establishment and maintenance of an adequate supply of pure water and drainage. Only in modern times has the necessity for a national water supply system relieved the Local Authorities of this burden. At the turn of the century Monmouthshire County Council realised that there would be a day of reckoning unless something was done about the inadequate fresh water supply to parts of the county. The mines and industry brought the people and both needed more water. The problem was further complicated by two factors: extensive mining had produced ground subsidence and the County waterworks began to show signs of settlement strains. Secondly, many of the towns are situated at a high altitude and above Abertillery the land rises to approximately 1300 feet above sea level. To gravity feed this area a very high impounding source had to be found. In 1906 the County Council sought advice from Mr. Baldwin Latham, an engineer with over forty years experience in sanitary and water engineering. Mr. Latham reported that no suitable source of supply could be found in Monmouthshire and at the nearest was over thirty miles away in the heart of the Black Mountains. The site selected for the water catchment and main reservoir was situated in the Grwyne Fawr Valley between the Gader and Ffwddog ridges. The actual impounding area was approximately two miles upstream from Shepherd Morgan's house at Blaen-y-cwm and twelve miles from the railway station at Llanfihangel Crucorney. At this time Blaen-y-cwm was without road access for wheeled traffic. Two hillside tracks descended into the valley to form one path through the ravine and over the mountain summit before descending again to Talgarth. The surveyors gained access to this remote spot from the Llanthony Valley along which was a reasonable road as far as the Priory Hotel with a track beyond to Capel-y-ffin. From here the only route was a climb over the mountain ridge to Grwyne Fawr, on foot or on horseback. In this way the rainfall was measured and the survey accomplished in 1906 and 1907. Mr. Latham's original proposal was for a pipeline to be laid from the base of the reservoir at approximately 1640 feet above sea level, along the mountainside through Fwthog Fawr to Dial Garreg before descending past the New Inn to Pont Esgob (Fforest), to Bettws, The Chain at Abergavenny and into the heart of the county. In 1908 Monmouthshire County Council promoted a Parliamentary Bill to enable them to obtain water from this source. The Bill was opposed and defeated. In fact the County was divided against itself, one part having an adequate supply of water, the other not. Why should those who had water pay rates for those with an inadequate supply. Innovation always causes controversy especially when the traditional pattern of life is threatened.

A ditty about the value of springs and wells summed up the argument at the time.

'Here I'm running free for all
And never for the rent I call,
But when you've water from the tap
You'll find you have to pay for that'

10

All the same, the thought of paying rates for someone else's benefit was revolutionary and a County Water Bill was without precedent. It had to fail. The next step was to form a Joint Water Board where the need was greatest using fresh plans based on the former survey. In 1909 the Urban District Councils of Abertillery (population 33,000), Abercarn (14,000), Risca (13,500) and Mynyddislwyn (10,000) sought Parliamentary power to sanction the Abertillery and District Water Board and in this way meet the urgent water requirements of their 70,000 people. By November further plans had been prepared and the new Bill was deposited in Parliament in December 1909. Messrs. T.S. Edwards & Son of Stow Hill, Newport, were the Board's Solicitors, Messrs. H.H. Tolson their Accountants and Messrs. Baldwin Latham & Son, Westminster their Engineers. Mr. Latham estimated that seven years would be required to complete the Works which included the highest masonry dam to be constructed in this country. The water was to be stored at approximately 1800 ft. above sea level.

FOOTNOTE:
Local inhabitants do not say "Grinney Four" but something like this — "Groyney-Vower". After about five years practice you might get it right, it's worth trying because the next valley is the Grwyne Fechan but over there it seems to be all one word — "Groyneyvechan".

11

Mr Matthews, Chairman of the Board

Birth Pangs

At the Lords

The House of Lords heard the Board's Bill read on 28th February and again on 7th March 1910 when a Select Committee was appointed to deal with it. Matters reached a climax in June when Mr. Honoratius Lloyd K.C. spoke as Counsel for the Bill with the Duke of Bedford in the chair. Referring to the plans Mr. Lloyd said *"Your Grace sees that we pass through a considerable track of country . . . through many districts and under the circumstances are all the elements for a magnificent Parliamentary fight. But I am happy to tell you that we have been able to look after all interests satisfactorily, both to them and to us. Your Grace will be troubled with only one single petition against the Bill"*. The objection came from the Abergavenny Town Council on two grounds: (i) that the scheme might interfere with their own water supply and, (ii) the Council was unwilling to accept water from the proposed Board on terms acceptable to the other districts served. There was some lively cross-examination. After a reference to the local lunatic asylum the Counsel for the objection pleaded, *"Be good-tempered with me"*, to which the Counsel for the Bill replied, *"I am quite good-tempered but I do think it most extraordinary for a little place like Abergavenny to come and put this district to the cost of opposing a Bill like this"*.

The Town Council had previously opposed the County Bill on the grounds that Abergavenny had an ample supply of water. *"But"*, said Mr. Lloyd, *"now that we are coming to Parliament at our own cost and they do not have to contribute a farthing they say they do need water! We knew it all the time, we knew it in 1908 and, your Grace, we know it now. Their water supply comes down from little ditches and gutters that flow into the Cibbi brook and this supply is not adequate, but, if they now want water we will supply them with water. I ask my learned friend to make up his mind, do not wobble about, you have told Parliament you do not need water and you have told Parliament that you do want water, make up your mind once and for all whether you do or do not. As for our interfering with the gutters from which your supply originates, it requires a trivial piece of engineering to avoid them altogether"*!

Their Lordship's concern was with Abergavenny only, where the Town Council expected preferential treatment from the Board, but this was not forthcoming. The town had a static population of about 8000, a vastly different situation from the developing industrial area over the mountain. Undoubtedly there would be periodical water shortages but the plea that the Council would have to look to the Board's source at Grwyne Fawr for further supplies" was absurd. Said Mr. Lloyd, *"They could not deal with this supply or do anything except swim in it and to talk about going up there to get 10,000 gallons a day is lunacy. The lunatic asylum is in the immediate neighbourhood"*.

His Grace listened impassively as 600 questions were fired across the floor but no agreement could be reached with the Town Council, *"and that, your Grace, means fighting the matter all over again"* (Mr. Lloyd). The Duke "cleared the committee room", conferred, called the Council and Petitioners in again and told them that the Bill would proceed. The Lords passed it on 4th July 1910 and the Board was over the first hurdle.

At the Commons

The Select Committee for the House of Commons heard objections from Messrs Lancasters Steam Collieries and the Llewellin Farm Trust, and both were of an unusual nature.

By now the collieries were long established. In addition to being riddled with underground workings, the Monmouthshire coal field still held about 1,270 million tons of 'black diamonds'.

At Abertillery in 1858, the former Monmouthshire Railway and Canal Co. had opened a mineral railway, serving ultimately five pits in the valley. These collieries commandeered stream water which flowed into the Ebbw Fach but soon the employees and their dependants numbering in thousands also needed fresh water.

Prior to 1894 the drainage and water supply for the area was in the hands of the Western Valleys Gas and Water Company and the Western Valley Sewerage Company. The latter Company laid a fifty mile sewer to the sea bed at Newport but without adequate water this sewer could not be connected. In 1894 the Abertillery Local Board purchased their section of the Gas and Water Co. and obtained an Act to build the 40 million gallon Cwmtillery compensating reservoir. This reservoir would guarantee Messrs Lancasters

Collieries 300,000 gallons a day and allow 400,000 gallons to be pumped out for domestic use. The arrangement was that the Colliery Co. should not mine below the reservoir site and allow the coal seam itself to support the reservoir area. However, Lancasters' workings encroached so close to the reservoir that soon after it was opened the sides began to subside and leak. This lost 90,000 gallons a day and the reservoir could not be filled, in case it burst. Lancasters then looked after themselves by tapping the water further upstream, but the sewer remained ineffective.

As there was now no way in which the Cwmtillery reservoir could be made water tight the Abertillery U.D.C. went to Parliament again in 1902 for power to construct another impounding reservoir further up the Tillery stream. To do this they entered into an agreement with the Llewellyn Trustees, holders of the Hendre Gwydin Farm, to purchase from them 42½ acres, but owing to the mining subsidences this scheme fell through. The agreed figure was no less than £100 an acre for poor quality grazing land, more than double the value of good farming land at this time. Though the figure was accepted the amount was undiluted greed.

So it was that when the newly created Board went to Parliament yet again in 1906 and finally in 1909 they had little or nothing to show for all their labour and expense and still they were opposed by Lancasters and by the Farm Trust.

The new Board no longer required 42½ acres and refused to pay £4,250 for unwanted land. The area required amounted to 2½ acres of rock outcrop to hold a small service reservoir with a capacity of 2 million gallons of Grwyne water. The Farm trustees lost their case.

The Lancaster colliery objection was more difficult and the persistent refusal of this company to share 'water rights' with their own work people makes lamentable reading. In his evidence, the local MP said that the inadequate water supply meant that it was not possible to use the sewer and at present the sewage "goes into a little stream and lies about on the banks". Mr. Lloyd concluded, *"That is the case for the Bill, sir"* and the Commons passed it on 28th July.

The Act of Parliament to constitute the Abertillery and District Water Board received Royal Assent on the 3rd August 1910, and it cost no less than £14,802.4.2., plus the large sums already expended in 1892, 1894 and 1902.

The scheme is described as —

"an Act to constitute and incorporate a Water Board consisting of the Councils of the Urban Districts of Abertillery, Abercarn, Risca and Mynyddislwyn in the County of Monmouth and to authorise the Board to construct waterworks to vest in the Board the waterworks undertakings of the said Councils and for other purposes. 10 Edw 7 and Geo 5". The estimated cost of the scheme was £251,000. Borrowed monies were to be repaid within sixty years and if the works were not completed within ten years the powers would lapse. The Act stipulated that 750,000 gallons of water must be allowed to flow down the stream each day, also that "a good and substantial road

14

bridge" must be built at Pontyspig to protect the rights of Mr. R. Baker-Gabb. Lord Glanusk must be allowed to boat and fish on the reservoir if he so desired. The Board was empowered to make and maintain *"twelve waterworks and other works in the Counties of Brecknock and Monmouth".*

These can be summarised as follows:—
Work No 1 was for "the great impounding reservoir to be called the Grwyne Fawr Reservoir".
Work No. 2 was for a catchwater drain to feed additional water into the reservoir.
Works Nos. 3 and 5 were for an aqueduct, conduit, line or lines of pipes from the Grwyne Fawr Reservoir to the parishes of Abertillery and Abercarn.
Works Nos. 4 and 6 were for service reservoirs at Cwmtillery and above Abercarn.
Work No. 7 was for a new road commencing in the parish of Lower Cwmyoy by a junction with the existing public road from Llanfihangel to Llanthony near the Queen's Head Inn, to Pont Esgob thence along the Grwyne Fawr Valley on the same alignment as the pipe line.
Work No. 8 was for a new bridle road above the Grwyne reservoir to replace a path which was to be flooded.
Work No. 9 was a road widening at Lower Stanton Farm corner.
Works Nos. 10 and 11 were for approach roads at Abertillery and Abercarn.
Work No. 12 was for a standard gauge railway siding, just over a quarter of a mile long, from a junction with the G.W.R. down main line near Llanfihangel station and terminating at the northern extremity of field No. 551 (Ordnance Survey 1901) near the Llanfihangel-Llanthony road. Such in outline were the authorised works together with "all necessary rails, junctions, turntables, embankments, walls, arches, scaffolding, machinery and apparatus".

With regard to Work No. 7 certain sections of the Act should be mentioned. Section 3 stipulated that the Board will *"within five years from the date of Assent construct a road 12 ft. at least in width, of which 9 ft. shall be metalled".* Section 11 says *"as soon as the Board have commenced the construction of the reservoir . . . they will proceed to construct a continuation of the said road . . . to the head or top of the reservoir";* Section 12 stipulates that the Board must construct the road with proper passing places, 18ft. at least in width and situated so far as is reasonably practicable within sight of one another and not more than half a mile apart. This was not practicable; it was simply impossible: The road was to be fenced or walled to the satisfaction of Lord Glanusk's agent. Finally, Section 15 required that *"Lord Glanusk, his Agents, tenants and commoners shall have the right at all times to use the said road and bridge with carts, horses, carriages and wagons, and to drive sheep and cattle along the same".* Thus the only means of communication between the Reservoir works and civilisation was along this new road. Let the prospective contractors take note of that. Stone was to be quarried and dressed on the site but the cement and all other supplies were to be transported by carts and traction engines from the field terminus of Work No. 12 to their destination, 10½ miles in all.

John Francis Jupp, Engineer.

A White Elephant

I n September 1910 the Board appointed Mr. Baldwin Latham as their Engineer. Clause two of their Agreement required the Engineer to employ and pay a Resident Engineer and Mr. Latham informed the Board that he had appointed his son John to fill this post. If the Contractor defaulted he would be responsible for the Resident Engineer's salary. Clause eleven specified that if the ageing Mr. Latham became incapacitated, or died before the Works were completed, then *"either he or his executors shall provide for the continuance of the contract"*. As Mr. George Latham also had a post, there was more than a suggestion of nepotism. In March 1911 John Francis Jupp, a name to be remembered, was made Surveyor to the Board.

Tenders were invited under three separate contracts, Nos. 1, 2 and 3. but what were the prospective contractors undertaking to build?

    (i)   A water main from the reservoir site to the two service reservoirs and then into the Board's District. To do this the Contractor must lay 33 miles of pipe below ground and bore a tunnel 1608 yards long through Coity mountain (between Waunavon and Cwmtillery). Once the main was completed the water supply would be available.

(ii)   A new road, approximately 10 miles in length into the heart of the mountains.

(iii)   The highest masonry reservoir in the country to store the water and guarantee the supply.

The above priorities are of interest. The first all-important stage was to have the water flowing through the main, and so recoup some capital by charging a water rate. Accountant Tolson had his eye on the revenue account. Storing the water in the main reservoir was the only way to guarantee a regular supply — but this was not the first priority.

On 8th June 1911 a 30-strong inspection party travelled to the site to have a look at the problems. They journeyed by 'brake' from Abergavenny to the hotel at Llanthony Priory for lunch, on to Capel-y-ffin Monastery, a further four miles where they "de-braked" to climb over the Ffwddog ridge in boiling heat. Some of the members were on the "shady side" of fifty. All would have to climb 1000ft. of mountain before descending to the reservoir site. The party included J.D. Latham, F. Jupp, Wm. Underwood, G.H. Walker and Abram Messam, the latter a very fat man. As the report puts it, "Their powers were tested". What is remarkable is that they all survived. They spent some time at the site and then walked back to the Monastery for the ride to Abergavenny. The journey emphasises the impossibility of getting wheeled traffic up the Grwyne valley before the new road was built. The only alternative would have been to leave the brakes at the Queen's Head Inn and travel on horseback along the mountain track to Blaen-y-cwm. Until the road was built, and occasionally afterwards, the official route to the Works was along the Llanthony Valley to Capel-y-ffin Monastery* and over the mountain.

In July the firm of William Underwood & Brother was at work testing the quality of the Grwyne Fawr stone and the summer months of 1911 kept many surveyors and prospective contractors busy. Meanwhile publicity conscious local councillors made speeches expressing their *"amazement at the slow progress in letting the contracts"*. At last the following notice appeared in the press: *"All tenders to be delivered to my office on or before 27th November 1911. T.S. Edwards, 24 Stow Hill, Newport"*.

FOOTNOTE
*This Monastery should not be confused with the ancient Priory ruin. It was built in 1871 by 'Father' Ignatius, an Anglican Deacon, in an attempt to restore the Order of St. Benedict in the Church of England. Ignatius died in 1908 and in 1911 an effort was being made to carry on his work. As The Monastery Church or Abbey had not been constructed properly it soon fell. Only the ruins now remain although the former monastic buildings are in use. Ignatius was buried at his Monastery and the place is well worth a visit together with a climb over the mountain to the reservoir "treading where the Board had trod".

Underwoods were the successful (or unfortunate) firm and they undertook to complete all three contracts in forty months at a cost of £261,745. In Parliament Mr. Latham had said seven years would be necessary and the Act itself allowed ten but William Underwood had other ideas and that was his first mistake.

Baldwin Latham, Engineer

The Board formally accepted Underwood's tender on 13th December, the contract was let in January 1912 the year that Dukinfield (in Cheshire) honoured Underwood by electing him Mayor of the Borough for the second time. His step-brother and partner, Mr. G.H. Walker, was placed in charge of the Works, under the Board's Engineer, and in the portly figure of Abram Messam the firm had an energetic Manager of the Works. Prospects seemed to be bright.

There had been one significant change to the plans passed by Parliament. In June 1911 the G.W.R. Company had offered to put in a new siding at Llanfihangel station; the Board accepted the offer and agreed to the terms. This meant that Work No. 12, the ¼ mile long siding and the only railway authorised by the Act was no longer necessary. The siding would have begun in the middle of nowhere on the main line between the Llanthony road bridge and Llanfihangel station, right in the mouth of a cutting and on a gradient of 1 in 100. The siding was to curve across the field to a loading bay near the Llanthony road and would have been difficult to work. There was much more to the offer of the G.W.R. Co. than met the eye. The Act specifically stated that before the junction with the main line railway could be effected the Board would have to obtain the permission of either the G.W.R. Secretary or the General Manager. In the circumstances it was unlikely that permission would be forthcoming, thus, while the Railway Company gained, the Board, and subsequently the Contractor, did not. The new G.W.R. siding at Llanfihangel station added nearly another mile to the road haulage, partly on a steep descent, and the contractor had to pay Abergavenny Rural District Council the cost of maintaining the lanes while the traction engines were running. This was an additional hazard.

Underwood set up his headquarters near the G.W.R. Station at Llanfihangel and his first task was to cut a new road 1¾ miles long from Lower Cwmyoy to Pont Esgob where it would meet the pipe line coming down the valley from the reservoir site, 8 miles away. The original idea of laying the conduit along the mountainside was abandoned in favour of the course below the new road. On this section the pipes had to be laid, the joints tested at 700 lb. per square inch, covered, and a road surface laid above them. With the road widening at Lower Stanton farm corner this would give the desired road access from Llanfihangel to Blaen-y-cwm and the dam.

Lower Cwmyoy, 14th February, 1912. Cutting the first sod of the new road.

The Board invited 196 guests for the cutting of the first sod of the new road at Lower Cwmyoy on 14th February 1912 and 102 turned up. Engineer Latham opened the proceedings, now a patriarchal old man with a long white beard. The cut was performed by Councillors G. Jones and F.J. Matthews, Chairman and Vice-Chairman respectively. William Underwood said this was the biggest job the firm had undertaken in 25 years of public work, while Abram Messam stood by waiting for action. The Rev. R.P. Dansey, Vicar of Kentchurch (near Pontrilas) prayed; he had meteorological interests and recorded the rainfall in the Grwyne Fawr Valley. After photographs the party went off to the Angel Hotel at Abergavenny for a champagne lunch and speeches. The liquor must have flowed like the Grwyne steam as it was confidently stated the water would be running in two years though the reservoir would take four to complete.

19

Guests were reminded that London once had an eye on Grwyne water but Monmouth had beaten them to it. Baldwin Latham inferred that he would have "bagged" it for Newport if he had known about the site before 1906. Congratulations all round. The work was now pushed ahead with great vigour and the contractor crossed the marshy ground at Cwm Coed y Cerrig (the valley of wood and stone) though not without difficulty. This stretch of land is a watershed between the Usk and the Wye Valleys and below the Twyn-y-Gaer and Bryn Arw hills brushwood fascines had to be laid in order to obtain a strong foundation for the road. Between Pont Esgob and Blaen-y-cwm the Contractor was able to make use of some existing lanes to farms in the valley though these had to be surveyed, graded and widened. An embankment was made over Nant Mair downstream from the old crossing which can still be traced near the gate to Ty'n Llwyn and another slight adjustment by the entrance to Penwyrlod. Two entirely new lengths of road were cut between Pont Esgob crossroads and Gwern y Bustach and further up between Neuaddwen and Coedias Bridge. (Map references for these, if required are 286211 to 283219 and 278239 to 273243.) It has not yet been established if the Rock Cutting at Cadwgan was a new cut or an improvement of the old one. 19th century maps indicate that the track was further from the river than the present road which is retained by a high wall dropping straight into the water. In a length of six miles from Pont Esgob to Blaen-y-cwm less than three miles was entirely new cut.

During 1912 materials arrived at Llanfihangel by rail and were carted by traction engines or by cart and four (horses) to Underwood's Depot at Lower Cwmyoy from there materials for Blaen-y-cwm had to be loaded on to pack horses and sent up the Mountain road from the Queen's Head Inn and down to the site of the prospective navvy village near Shepherd Morgan's house, six miles away. At one time a man from Llangattock used a team of mules to transport materials along the road, later a haulier from Llanfoist tried a cart pulled by three horses but he could not get beyond the Ffawydd farm (1½ miles short of Blaen-y-cwm).

Underwood set up another depot at Pont Esgob (Fforest) so that he could construct the new road from each end simultaneously, and also commence his conduit up the valley and around the east side of the Sugar Loaf mountain. The public road route to Pont Esgob was from Llanfihangel station yard to the hamlet of Pant-y-Gelly then along the lane between Sugar Loaf and Bryn Arw mountains via Bettws and down to Pont Esgob. There were steep hills at Pant-y-Gelly, each side of Bettws and a fierce descent past the Globe Inn to Pont Esgob. In muddy weather the "road" surface would not stand the traction engine drive and the wheels churned into the mud until the firebox was on the ground.

Underwood planned to construct the Works by employing a huge army of navvies. The word 'navvy' is a contracted form of navigator and was originally used to describe the men who built the canals. From the waterways the navvies progressed to railways and water works — but the name stuck to them. Great squads of navvies moved about the country wherever pick and shovel work was to be found. They included a large number of Irish labourers who seemed able to subsist on a diet of fresh air, bread and cheese, beer and whisky.

The navvies were remarkable, independent men who catered for themselves and never stayed long on one job. And — could they work! It was an unwritten code of navvy conduct never to be late on the job. If by any chance a man failed to be at work by 6.00 a.m. (summer) and 8.00 a.m. (winter) he automatically reported to the office and asked for his 'cards' (insurance).

It was a navvy custom to have a wage 'sub' each day, with the result that his Friday pay packet was very 'light'. This habit originated in the old days when many small contractors went bankrupt, without warning, and the navvy had to protect himself as best he could. The description of a new job might read *"Muck near the waggons, sub. every night, sleep on the job".* What more could you want?

Manager Messam kept his navvies hard at work though he had problems. By now the Insurance Acts had been passed and on a Board Inspection visit to Fforest in August 1912 the following situation was reported: a man had started work, received his cards and worked for half an hour. He was not satisfactory and Abram sacked him. Pay for the half hour was 3d but the stamps cost 9d and the man's share was 5d, so after half an hour's work he owed the firm 2d! The navvies got to know Messam and composed their own ditties about him:

"Old Messam comes up to watch us each day
Curses all round and give us our pay
So off to Aber we go straightaway
And tomorrow tramp back to make the roadway".

The verse means the men drank their earnings in Abergavenny, slept it off and then returned to the job. Abram started them again either because he didn't know who they were or because he could not get anyone else. Another jingle went like this:

"Among the Black Mountains,
Along the roadway
Paying 4d a night
To sleep on old Hay".

Though these were early days of motoring some people realised that the future of transport lay with the motor car. The 1903 Act of Parliament permitted the speed of cars to be increased from 14 mph to 20 mph but still restricted them to 10 mph in the towns. The well-to-do were driven around by their chauffeurs and several local people had already become 'two car types'. Lord Llangattock of the Hendre owned a fleet of five, consisting of a Rolls Royce, a Humber, a Daimler and two Panhards. R.W. Kennard still used a White steam car. William Underwood visited the various sites in his chauffeur-driven car, Baldwin Latham travelled around in a Fiat and Messam owned a Darracq. The latter made motoring history when he visited the cashier, Clifford Harris, at Gelli Welltog farm, high above Pont Esgob. Abram was declared to be the first motorist to drive up the 'pitch', a task which still requires some skill with the gear lever. All this added up to big news at the Globe Inn at Fforest, which did a roaring trade, but who could supply the contractor with suitable lorries? That was the important question.

By the 16th October 1912 the work was sufficiently advanced for a party of 150 to travel along the new road to the site of the dam for the next sod cutting session. Most people travelled by brake though some motors were present. On this occasion the ceremony was performed by Councillor F.J. Matthews of Abercarn, now the Board's Chairman, assisted by the Vice Chairman, Councillor David Lewis of Risca.

William Underwood, car and road roller.

In places the pipe laying was not yet finished and the surface was temporary, so were the bridges at Pont Esgob and Blaen-y-cwm. Lady Glanusk was there. This time the party adjourned to a temporary corrugated iron building for an excellent cold luncheon. Baldwin Latham rose to "musical honours" and reported landowner Baker-Gabbs' pleasure with the progress of the work and the behaviour of the men. He also said that Lord Glanusk had sold the fifty acre reservoir site at a nominal sum and donated the land needed for the pipe and road. 533 men were engaged on the project and the Rev. D. Felix chose this auspicious moment to make a successful appeal for the Navvy mission. Once again everyone was supremely optimistic. The formula was: water in the hills + wine in the stomach = a piped supply next year and the dam in two or three years. Most of the guests would not live to see the opening day.

The Monmouthshire Evening Post reported the event as follows: *"The valley lying quiet in its secluded beauty has hitherto been practically inaccessible and as the site of the proposed reservoir lies a good ten miles up the valley, it was imperative that the first work undertaken should be a road of that length. The difficulty of such an engineering feat could only be realised by one who has walked the valley from end to end. The roadway which starts at Lower Cwmyoy . . . crosses the stream in two places. A large number of retaining walls had to be erected . . . one portion goes through a deep rock cutting . . . the inspection party noted with admiration the engineering triumph of Mr. Baldwin Latham with the aid of the contractors and navvies."*

During 1912 a picturesque feature was the large number of tents dotted along the valley following the course of the pipeline. As yet the men did not have permanent living quarters and the white canvas contrasted with the green pasture. It was a particularly attractive sight when viewed from Penwyrlod farm. Supplying the workmen with food was difficult and the farmer's wife soon organised extra supplies. Food was brought out to the mill at Pont Esgob and transported up the pitch past Gelli Welltog then on to Partrishow and along the mountainside track to Penwyrlod. Bread was baked at this farm and supplies were then distributed to the workmen in the district below.

Mr. Thomas of Abergavenny transported men in a horse drawn vehicle along the vale of Ewyas as far as the Half Moon Inn at Llanthony. From here they had to walk over the mountain to the site of the village, where there was at least one hut which could sleep ten men. It also contained a long table, normally drawn up to the ceiling and let down at meal times.

Living quarters and other facilities for the men employed at Blaen-y-cwm became a pressing problem in 1912. In June the Board's Committee heard of proposals to build a canteen and a brewery firm came in with the offer to build a mission hall if given the licence for the canteen (!) but the proposition was lost by three votes to twelve. The Board subsequently relented and the canteen plans were passed on the 30th October 1912 with Abram Messam as the first licensee. The pressure for the canteen came from the Chief Constable of Brecon who said the absence of facilities would result in "shebeening" (the unauthorised house selling of drink.)

The horses were now laid off and breathed again but there was no breathing space for the Mayor of Dukinfield. Before the whole length of the road was finished the traction engines began to knock up the surface, especially on the steep gradients. After the opening the traffic increased and so did the problems. The machines stuck on the muddy sites, occasionally turned over and sometimes the drivers lost control on the steep descent from Llanfihangel station to Stanton farm. They had to drive the machine into the bank to stop it. At the end of 1912 Underwood approached the Board about the difficulty and suggested that a railway or tramway should be laid on the road surface. There were problems; no railway was authorised, there was not enough room for both railway and public roadway, the gradients were considered too steep and the Board had no private road for the last 1½ miles to Llanfihangel. This meant that no rails could be laid on this section. The contractor increased the thickness of the road surface from 6″ to 9″ and the traction engines helped themselves to the extra three inches. By 1913 His Worship was in real trouble. The attempt to reach the site without a railway had failed, this was another mistake which proved to be a costly one (see appendix III Road & Rail in 1910).

"Duckinfield"

A Duck in the Field

I f locomotives were able to tackle the steep gradients could a railway be laid down on the Board's new road? The Act of 1910 contained a remarkable "1845 Railways Clauses Consolidation Act" section which apparently allowed a railway to be laid anywhere on the ground within the permitted boundaries of the Works. (See Appendix vi). In 1913 this meant salvation to Engineer Latham and Contractor Underwood. There was nothing to prevent the firm laying a railway along their road surface for according to the 1845 Act almost anything could be defined in terms of a railway. The Board authorised Underwood to lay a 3ft. gauge 'tramway' from Lower Cwmyoy and to negotiate with local landowners for powers to extend the track across the fields to Llanfihangel Yard. The Contractor also had to arrange with the Abergavenny Rural District Council for the crossing of two public roads — at his own expense.

The first hint of the troubled times ahead came early in 1913 when Underwood was behind schedule with the Coity Mountain tunnel. Only 650 of the 1608 yards had been completed. The Inspection Committee urged the need to work three eight hour shifts or else to sub-contract and reported to the Board that "it is not the construction of the road, or the Dam or the railway but the construction of Coity tunnel that is the most important matter. Something must be done or the water cannot go on and the rates will be burdened". The tunnel was not finished until 1915.

The main pipeline was laid beneath the road until it was diverted across the valley to the reservoir base. Pipe laying was later facilitated by the use of specially adapted "dobbin" carts as "ro-railers". These carts had three wheels and were pulled by two horses, one each side of the centre shaft. The rear wheels had small flanges for the 3ft. gauge rails and the centre wheel ran on a row of planks laid between the rails. In this way the carts could be used either on or off the rails where pipes were being unloaded and submerged.

In February 1913 Underwood began to lay the railway track from Lower Cwmyoy. The eight miles to Blaen-y-cwm would require the stipulated 16 half mile crossing places for rail and road traffic. Although the railway was laid to the left side of the road many places were too narrow to allow both types of traffic to be worked safely. In April the Committee walked from Cwmyoy to Fforest (Pont Esgob) and noted, *"It is impossible for a conveyance to pass along the road without going over the sleepers"*. This meant that the next inspection party must travel to the dam via Llanthony, Capel-y-ffin and over the mountain. This route included a call for lunch at the Llanthony Hotel and one wonders if all members of the Committee travelled further than the hostelry. In 1913 the Water Board owned only one car which was temporarily out of action owing to a broken spring. This made it necessary to *"hire cars"* for the officials travelling to the site of the Works in April and May 1913.

By the 14th April 1913 four miles of rail had been laid taking the railhead into the Partrishow area and six miles remained. On this date it was reported that the Pont Esgob bridge was finished but not that at Blaen-y-cwm. The Committee was informed that 80 wagons were on the line and that there were 80 more in the yard at Llanfihangel. It was also reported that three locomotives had arrived. Such was the information, there was no confirmation. 160 wagons was far beyond the traffic requirements and only two locomotives worked on the line in the contractor's time. It is possible that Underwood kept a spare engine at Llanfihangel while he tried to obtain land for the line across the fields to Lower Cwmyoy. This he failed to do and the first railway remained isolated until 1919. Two locomotives were ample for the traffic and if there was a third there would have been no point in manoeuvring it along the lanes until there was work to be done.

The railhead was gradually pushed further up the valley and in July the trains were within half a mile of the Blaen-y-cwm huts, waiting for the bridge to be finished. On 17th September 1913 Messrs. Latham, Messam and Edwards drove to Lower Cwmyoy and then rode to the dam on the locomotive footplate, noting the slow progress of the Works. Only twenty five men were at work on the dam. Thus September 1913 can be taken as the opening date of the first railway that ran into the Black Mountains instead of around them. Lower Cwmyoy, Cwm Coed-y-Cerrig, Fforest, Gelli Welltog, Gwern-y-Bustach, Partrishow, Ty Isaf and Blaen-y-cwm now resounded to the echo of the locomotive exhaust and whistle reverberating across the valley.

Underwood supplied locomotives ANITA and DUKINFIELD to work the traffic which required considerable skill. There were some awful spots. Coming down the valley with the empties, the short 1 in 19 incline up to Gwern-y-Bustach had to be rushed, but once over the summit the driver was

immediately on the steep descent for half a mile or so to Pont Esgob Bridge beyond which was a very sharp left curve. Drivers had to learn the road by experience. The late Mr. Thomas Parsons never forgot his wedding day. He left Gelli Welltog farm at 5.30 a.m. on 25th June 1913 to be in good time for the service at Bethany Church, Abergavenny. At the bottom of the "pitch" he passed the new railway with engine DUKINFIELD off the rails and on its side at Pontyspig farm. Driver Frank Ward was scalded and sitting in the field with his head in his hands. He had come down the bank too fast for the bend. DUKINFIELD derailed on several occasions and was notoriously unsteady. After the war the fitters at Blaen-y-cwm increased the size of the water equalising pipe under the saddle tank and added a second pipe in an attempt to stabilise the engine.

Although the ANITA looked the neater of the two it was the DUKINFIELD that caught the eye of the young farmers. Proudly named after His Worship's home town in Cheshire, the place was unknown to the Welsh Border farmer. The name could have but one meaning, it was short for "a duck in the field". Any doubt was removed when the ungainly machine left the rails and waddled into the field on that June morning back in 1913.

Engine sheds were built at Lower Cwmyoy and Blaen-y-cwm, but Cwmyoy was the place; it had an inspection pit and a water tower. *"Whistling Jack"* was the mechanic, Messrs. Ward and Mole did the engine driving and Dai Lewis was the "rope runner", i.e. fireman and shunter. Arthur Atkins drove the traction engine from the G.W.R. yard.

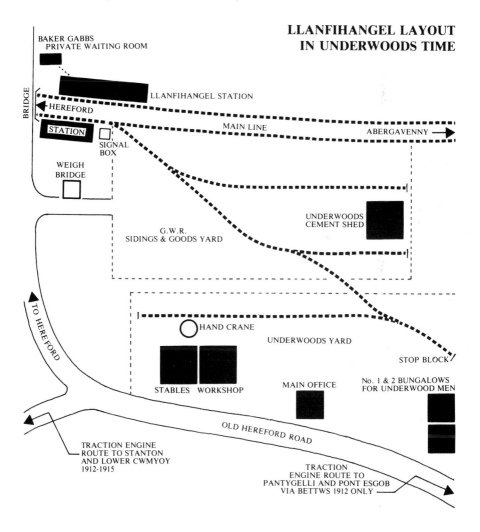

LLANFIHANGEL LAYOUT IN UNDERWOODS TIME

Cement and other materials for Blaen-y-cwm and Grwyne Fawr Works were transferred from the G.W.R. at Llanfihangel to either traction engines or cart and horses. Underwood's headquarters were between the old Hereford Road and the G.W.R. siding at Llanfihangel. The buildings included an office with three rooms, one pair of dwelling huts, stables, blacksmith's and carpenter's shops and a large cement shed. The equipment included three derrick cranes and a saw bench. The first section of the journey was 1½ miles along the public lane to the Llanthony Road junction at Lower Stanton farm, here Work No. 9 can be seen being a castellated farm wall where the road had to be widened to let the traffic through. The railhead was reached immediately after the turn into the Board's road at Lower Cwmyoy and at this depot transhipment was made again from road back to rail. In addition to the engine shed there was a "run round" loop and a long siding on the Llwyncelyn farm side of the road.

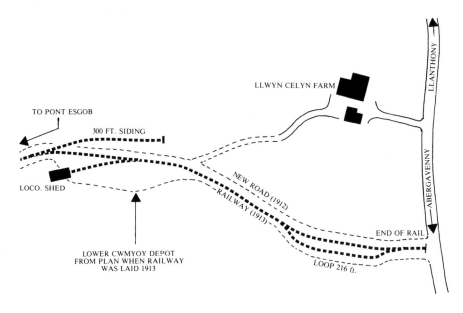

The next 1½ miles is a gap between the Twyn-y-Gaer and Bryn Arw hills. The first three passing places (hereafter designated "p.p.") for rail and road traffic were on this section. At Pont Esgob a sharp right hand curve brought the track over the pipeline. Here there was another short siding to provide a loading depot for materials arriving via the lanes from Llanfihangel and Bettws, that is if they arrived. After crossing the stream there was the steep ascent to Gwern-y-Bustach farm through p.p. 12. At the summit there was a short trailing siding followed by the dramatic descent to the Nant Mair stream and p.p. No. 11. P.p. No. 10 was near Coed farm beyond which there was a siding. Coed Dias house came into view on the right near p.p. 9. Here the track is in the ravine and almost at river level. Switchback gradients followed through p.p.'s 8 to 5 at Ty Isaf; after p.p. 2 the track crossed the river, passed shepherd

Morgan's house and climbed steeply to the village. At Blaen-y-cwm the layout included a locomotive shed and passing loop. P.p. 1 was on the new road to the reservoir top but no rails were laid on this section. The railway track continued along the bottom of the valley for about two miles to reach the catchment area and crossed the stream again en route. At the reservoir site the railway was located to the east or left of the later route. It was carried above the site of the foundation of the dam wall by a 60ft. long wooden trestle bridge and then crossed the stream to reach the mason's yard.

1913 was a bad year for Underwood & Brother. The firm could not make progress with Coity Mountain tunnel, it was lumbered with a railway and struggling with labour problems. Latham's estimated seven years to build the works was a sound figure, the agreed forty months was not. Recruiting and supplying a labour force of up to 1000 men proved to be an impossible task, particularly as many had to be quartered at Blaen-y-cwm as yet without houses, telephone, postal or medical services. The main burden for all this fell on the shoulders of William Underwood and in July 1913 the Board censured him on account of the slow progress with all the Works. In October the Inspection Committee reported an improvement but in December it was again "extremely dissatisfied". The Board threatened to enforce full penalties if Underwood did not finish on time. Lack of experience with this type of work meant that William Underwood was no match for the professional expertise of Messrs. Latham and Edwards but the former mayor of Dukinfield was undaunted. As events worked out another factor emerged about which there was nothing in the contract, the Great War. The Board would not be able to blame Underwood & Brother for that!

At the Reservoir, Underwood used a quarry near the foundation of the Dam where he installed a large electrically powered stone breaking machine and a sand crusher driven by a portable steam engine. Unfortunately his electrical plant was not sufficiently powerful for the work.

The contractor was always struggling at the Dam. In 1913 his Manager was employing stonemasons at 8½d an hour instead of 9d and worse, some were taken on at 9d and paid off at 8½d. This did not attract men to the job. By the end of the year things had improved and 51 men were at work on full trade union rates of pay. Seven derrick cranes operated near to the line of foundation.

Unfortunately no-one knew how to deal with the reservoir foundation and there are recurring references to this problem. Mr. G.H. Walker reported, *"The strata of rock is entirely different from what we had been led to expect from the trial bores. Solid rock appeared much nearer the surface than as shown on the contract drawings. Expert attention is needed to make sure that the foundation is watertight".*

Surprisingly, plans were now put in hand to build another reservoir and the Board's second Act of Parliament received Royal Assent on 8th July 1914. This enabled them to build the Helyg reservoir between the Grwyne Fawr Works and Blaen-y-cwm village, taking water from the Nant-yr-Helyg and the Nant-yr-Gader Fawr streams. The rapid rise in the population figure was the official reason for this Helyg scheme but as the estimated population increases had already been worked out in 1909/10 it seems odd that a further reservoir was required in 1913. It is significant that the preamble to the Act refers to *"unexpected geological features"* at the site of the main reservoir and to the need for unspecified "additional works". Equally significant is the power granted to borrow no less than £250,000, an amount almost equal to the estimated total cost of the original scheme. The Act allowed ten years for building this Helyg reservoir but the work was never started and in July 1915 the Minute Books refer to the "abandonment of the Helyg scheme".

The Inspection Committee continued to visit the Works via the Llanthony Hotel and the Monastery. As late as 19th November 1913 they went over the mountain to Grwyne Fawr. As the railway had by now been opened throughout for over two months it *"must have been a beautiful morning"*, but Blaen-y-cwm became demanding and after 1913 leisurely excursions via Llanthony had to be exchanged for a "shake-up" in the train. One man who

Shepherd Morgan's House.

FOOTNOTE
The Minutes refer to 80 wagons on the line and 80 more at Llanfihangel yard. These figures were reported by the Inspection Committee after their visit on the 16th April 1913. They are probably a misprint for 8 as no more than about 16 wagons could have been in use at this time.

30

BLAEN·Y·CWM VILLAGE
GRWYNE FAWR WORKS
SEPT. 1914

Built by William Underwood and Brother.

must have had more than enough of the mountain track was Mr. Robert Parker. The Board appointed him their Inspector of the Works at Grwyne Fawr in December 1912 but his house had not then been built. Mr. Parker lodged at Chapel farm, Capel-y-ffin, and made the double journey over the mountain each day until he could take up residence in May 1913.

Blaen-y-cwm is significant. It was near here that the ancient mountain tracks descended into the valley and the traveller bound for central Wales had to use the ravine. The path took him through the reservoir site and along the Rhiw Cwmstabl (the constable's steep ascent) to the top of the escarpment. This route was well trodden and in 1188 Archbishop Baldwin of Canterbury used it.

Accompanied by Gerald the Welshman his party was travelling from Talgarth to Abergavenny recruiting for the Third Crusade. They found the track wild and bleak, not to mention dangerous. Partrishow would be a welcome haven. In 1910 Blaen-y-cwm was shepherd Morgan's house. Today the barn is unchanged while the house has been beautifully preserved and whoever holds the property holds Blaen-y-cwm, the house at the head of the valley. Between 1912 and 1928 Blaen-y-cwm was knocked about a bit. First came the new road, then a railway and finally the village.

31

At Navvyville

T he first *'law of the works'* was 'the more remote the site the more important is the navvy village'. The Grwyne Fawr Reservoir site was nothing if not remote and the navvy task force would be dependant on their temporary homes, stores, canteen, hospital and school not to mention the doctor, the policeman, and the pastor.

The village was located two miles below the Reservoir and near the Morgan's house, Blaen-y-cwm. The huts were made of wood covered outside with corrugated iron and were snug in winter. From their appearance arose the name *"tin town"* but that was unofficial. The Board called the place the *"Navvy Village"*, locally it was Blaen-y-cwm village or just *"The Village"*.

The navvies were warm-hearted fellows. When a *"fresher"* arrived in the canteen *"on tramp"* he was normally accepted as "one of them" and the hat went round to get him established. The navvies knew their men; the hobnailed boots, corduroy trousers, 'Yorks' and muffler were the authenticating evidence of the genuine type. Recognition was much the same over at Hay-on-Wye, the home of Dr. Hincks. When a stranger arrived in the town the first question was *"Is he a gentleman?"*. The right tie and accent usually meant social acceptance. The differences between The Hay and The Navvy Village were purely circumstantial.

The construction of forty dwelling huts began in 1913 but only fifteen were built before the work had to cease as a wartime measure. Abram Messam employed cheap labour (5½d an hour *'botty gangs')* but the hut keepers complained that these men were too dirty and could not live with the others. They had to leave. As labour was hard to obtain the Board agreed to a policy of segregation and opened a *"common lodging house"* in September 1913. This consisted of two corrugated iron circular buildings each with a stove in the middle. The beds were all arranged 'foot to stove' and at the Village these roundhouses were referred to as 'doss houses'. The canteen was opened on 24th July 1913 and immediately became the Village social centre. Several small shops were available in the Village including Mrs. Lewis Morgan's sweet shop.

Once again the Chief Constable of Breconshire stepped in and informed the Board that he had appointed a policeman to the Village — at their expense. Constable Dew took up his duties in July, lodging at the canteen. His concrete police station was not opened until 1915. Progress was hampered because originally the Village was without a telephone or postal service. Both were installed late in 1913 and the contractor had to pay for the telephone.

In May 1913 Councillor Nash reported that there were a number of children living at Blaen-y-cwm. He explained to the Committee that under the Education Act the Board must repay Breconshire County Council the cost of building, staffing and maintaining a Day School.

Blaen-y-cwm School. An early post-war photograph with 39 children present.

The only site available was on the west bank of the Grwyne stream which would separate the school from the village. Access was to be by means of a footbridge. Four Foundation or Board Managers were appointed plus two from the County Council and it took them six months to get the plans off the ground. In January and March 1914 the Managers reported that "the school and the schoolmaster's house are under construction" — with accommodation for sixty children.

The opening day was fixed for 18th May 1914 and the Board travelled up in strength for the ceremony. First there was a charabanc which ran through the Western Valleys collecting members en route to Brynmawr, and went on to Abergavenny and Lower Cwmyoy. Here Messam had a locomotive and three carriages waiting to take the party on the 7½ mile run to the Village. As the train charged up the last incline the waiting school children cheered. The Vice-Chairman declared the school open and handed it over to the staff, Mr. & Mrs. Vincent Feathers of Dowlais, both certificated, of course, with Constable Dew a natural choice for the Attendance Officer. The party then adjourned to the 'Hotel de Grwyne' (the canteen) where the licensee, Abram Messam, had laid on lunch.

The 1910 Act included protective clauses to ensure that the law was kept and that education was provided for the children of employees, but no provision was made for the spiritual needs of the workpeople.

With most large Public Works contracts it was customary to appoint a resident missioner to look after the religious and social life of the community. These missioners were trained men who did not belong to any denomination and they were employed by an organisation known as the Navvy Mission. While their importance was unquestioned the position of the missioner was sometimes obscure; was he responsible to the Mission, the Board or the Contractor? Much depended on who paid the major part of his salary.

In June 1912 the Board granted the Navvy Mission permission to "erect a mission hall near the site of the proposed reservoir" and instructed their clerk to obtain the sanction of the Local Government Board to pay one-third of the cost of the hall and one-third of the *"missionaries"* salary. Later in the year they heard that the Rev. Felix was *"endeavouring to raise £54 for the expense of a missioner to work between Cwmtillery and Risca"*.

Meanwhile news of the project reached Budleigh Salterton, Devon, where it touched the heart of philanthropist Miss Moulton Barratt who also wished to *"erect huts and reading rooms for the men"*. The Board agreed to both projects and passed on the responsibility to the Contractor, whereupon Miss Barratt withdrew as she saw no need for both ventures.

In October Underwood submitted his plan for the mission hall but the Navvy Mission also required a stone built house for their missioner. This brought things to a head and the Board refused to pay any of the costs involved while the Contractor declined to build a *'manse'*. He was left with the hall which was opened in 1913 with a Canadian couple, Mr. & Mrs. Leach, in charge. It was their job to look after the postal arrangements.

The Act also made it clear that the Board had a legal responsibility to Breconshire County Council for the medical welfare of the men employed on the Works and early in 1913 Dr. Thomas E. Hincks became the Blaen-y-cwm panel doctor. Dr. Hincks practised at Hay-on-Wye and as the Works and Village did not have a telephone he was completely cut off from his patients. The shortest route from Hay to the Village was over the Gospel Pass and down to Capel-y-ffin, then over the top of the Ffwddog ridge and down to the Village, a daunting 10 mile ride for the doctor who was an excellent horseman.

In June 1913 the Inspection Committee met the Doctor on site. He told them it was absolutely essential to have a qualified nurse/midwife at the Village and a telephone line to Hay. This was agreed. The doctor also said that his surgery must be enlarged so that there would *"be room for the bad cases"*. Finally he appealed for an isolation hospital.

Back in Newport the Board agreed to pay Hincks a £50 per annum retention fee and characteristically "urged the contractor to make a contribution" (there was no legal reason why he should). In April 1914 Dr. Hincks met a Special Committee at the Angel Hotel, Abergavenny where *"he spoke at great length"*. The Doctor first of all charmed the Committee by pointing out that "the present nursing arrangements are most satisfactory" (little else was at this time) and then presented his case for the 'Blaen-y-cwm & District General Hospital' as it might have been called, complete with isolation unit and mortuary.

Dr. Hincks said that the Abergavenny Cottage Hospital had declined to treat navvies and that Hereford Hospital was a long way off. Even supposing Abergavenny was co-operative (for once) patients would still have to be transported along the Board's railway line and transhipped at Lower Cwmyoy. He had considered suspending stretchers from the roof of an ambulance type coach but the overall arrangement was not satisfactory (see Appendix iv). At this point the Contractor, already in trouble with the Works, decided to score some points and came in with an offer to defray half the cost of the hospital unit.

The delighted Special Committee reported to their Board at Newport and the plan was unanimously agreed, on the shared cost basis. The building was opened in 1915, and consisted of two wards, a surgery, a consulting room, and living quarters for Nurse Bowkett who had been at the Village for a year.

Dr. Hincks shortly after then went off to the War.

It is sometimes difficult to reconcile the various statements made, not because of what is minuted but because of what is not. For example, as late as mid-1914 Dr. Hincks requests this full medical unit which the Board and Contractor agree to supply. At the same time all work is due to be finished by mid-1915 (the year in which the hospital opened). So on the one hand the Board have to threaten the Contractor with dire penalties if he does not achieve the impossible and finish on time; on the other hand, both parties cheerfully open up the hospital unit. The confusion is evident and with World War I now well in its stride, both were in for a rough time.

Between 200 and 300 men, women and children were now living at Blaen-y-cwm. The main work was to complete the pipe laying and lay the foundation of the reservoir thirty feet below the stream. In May 1914 a gas engine was brought up the line to drive the dynamo for generating electricity. Most of the pipes were supplied by the British Mannesman Tube Co. of Newport, a firm which had its headquarters in Germany. Their method of jointing was not satisfactory and years later Francis Jupp *"wished he had never seen a German pipe"*. J.D. Latham and G. Remington paid a visit to Dusseldorf seeking a solution to the problem. Meanwhile the Board appointed Mr. S. Foster Deacon of Blaenavon, Monmouthshire, as their Superintendent Water Engineer at a salary of £150 per annum, paid by the Contractor!

The outbreak of war had no immediate effect on the Works. The run-down came later, but the Contractor's time was running out. On 1st January 1915 there was still no sign of the reservoir wall and Coity Mountain tunnel was not finished. However, all was not yet lost. The trains were running over the impossible gradients and other 'impossibles' might yet be overcome. William Underwood applied for an extension of time.

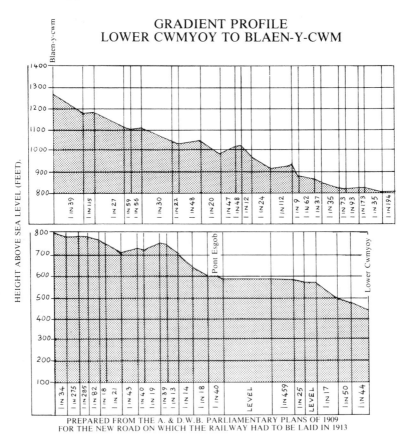

GRADIENT PROFILE
LOWER CWMYOY TO BLAEN-Y-CWM

PREPARED FROM THE A. & D.W.B. PARLIAMENTARY PLANS OF 1909
FOR THE NEW ROAD ON WHICH THE RAILWAY HAD TO BE LAID IN 1913

William Underwood, Contractor

At the end of time

By 1915 the obstacles were not overcome and under war-time conditions no contractor could obtain the type of labour Underwood required. Beaten by the calendar and the political situation, he was not yet beaten in spirit. He fought on and in spring 1915 Coity Mountain surrendered. The resistance here had been due to a geological fault in the rock which has continued to cause trouble to successive generations of engineers.

On 1st April 1915 Superintendent Engineer Francis Jupp was able to inform his Board that water was running through the pipeline to the service reservoirs. Since this date the Board's district has been fed with Grwyne Fawr water. The supply came from a small dam near the northern extremity of the Works. This dam remains and alongside it can be seen Underwood's temporary meter house with the mains pipe below the floor. From here the pipe travelled along the east side of the area to be flooded and four feet below the ground, on an alignment just above the proposed high water level. When it reached the site of the masonry wall the pipe descended the valley side to the site of the main valve at 1637 ft. above sea level. From this point the pipeline crossed the valley to join the new public road at 1590 ft. which it then followed down to Blaen-y-cwm and along the valley bottom to Pont Esgob. When the main reservoir supply was connected, the original pipeline around the side of the reservoir was cut off but not removed. During Underwood's time and throughout the construction period there were two meter houses. The small one referred to above measured the water fed to the Board's district and the large building outside the foundation of the wall metered the downstream water flow. When the reservoir was opened both supplies were measured in the latter building.

Everything appeared to be going well for William Underwood & Brother. The Inspection Committee was *"pleased with the Works generally"* and they *"much appreciated the efforts* being made for the benefit of the workpeople" who now enjoyed hot baths, concerts, draughts, dominoes, cards, a library, a reading room and a quoits pitch! In just over three years the Contractor had completed eleven of the twelve Works authorised. The exception was *"the great impounding reservoir"* itself of which very little could yet be seen.

In 1910/11 costing work was done with some labour rates of pay as low as 4¾d an hour. By 1915 some rates were as high as 9d an hour. G.H. Walker reported to the Board that the contractor was losing £1,000 a month. Another problem was the weather; our study has already referred to the heavy rainfall, ideal for a reservoir but not for outdoor construction. In January Mr. Walker reported that out of 87 recent days 51 were wet. Little allowance seems to have been made for this or for complete stoppage in mid-winter.

Behind the scenes lynx-eyed officials studied figures and dates. Their Accountant reminded the Board that Underwood was now £93,000 of work behind schedule. Their solicitor informed them that the contract was let in January 1912 and that it expired on the 6th June 1915. They enquired what the Board proposed to do about an extension of time and who was going to pay their salaries?

In July 1915 the Board made a formal indictment to which Underwood politely replied that they could not possibly be in full possession of the facts and he asked to meet a sub-committee. Reporting to this Committee Underwood spoke of bad rock, bad weather and bad labour. He admitted that no work had been done to the reservoir for five months. The following figures show the total number of men employed on the Works and indicate the extent of the labour problem.

1913	January 395	March 512	July 466	December 315
1914	January 295	August 279	Sept. 227	
1915	June 146	Sept. 104	Oct. 73	November 56

The Contractor reminded the Board that although he had no desire to shift responsibility from his own shoulders the War was not yet over. He advocated suspension of the Works. Baldwin Latham ignored the War and was for pushing on at all costs. His arguments were based on contracts and money but they bore little relation to the stark facts. Latham was now an old man; he retired in December 1915 and died in 1919. John Francis Jupp succeeded him as Chief Engineer, a post he held until his retirement 21 years later.

In November 1915 the Board agreed with the Contractor to suspend the Works as from 31st December and until two months after peace was declared. All plant was to be left on the site apart from anything requisitioned by the Ministry of Munitions and was to be kept in good order by the Contractor. In May 1916 the Inspection Committee reported that the Contract or was removing plant from the Works. Underwood explained that he needed it at the Penderyn Works and that the cranes were not suitable for the Grwyne Fawr construction. He also asked permission to sell two locomotives for £320 and this was agreed. No details of the engines are given. One was probably the third or spare machine already referred to, the other used on a service reservoir railway or siding.

In July 1916 Underwood met the Board again, informing them that his step-brother G.H. Walker had died. He was prepared to continue and in a frank statement said he had been informed that he could still make £20,000 out of the job. However he was getting older, there was no sign of the end of hostilities and when the War did finish there would be much non-contract work before construction could re-start. Personally he thought it would be in the best interests of both parties for the Board to take over but in any case they must take expert advice as to just *"how they stood"* in the matter. The expert advice required was two-fold, geological and financial. Without Latham's experience Messrs. Jupp and Underwood found themselves asking more questions about the foundation of the reservoir than they could answer. With regard to finance Underwood admitted that his position was *"serious"* and pointed out that the Board was in the same situation!

He spoke of the harmonious relationships that he had enjoyed with the Board and reiterated his willingness to continue the work. (Stories about the contractor going bankrupt are not true). Finally Underwood reminded the Board that the initial delays were due to the unsuitability of their road — which he had re-surfaced at his own cost.

In November 1916 the Board received the Contractor's valuation of all the equipment in his possession.

The value of all the items listed by Underwood totalled £197,000 but he finally agreed to accept £30,000 for the lot. On 1st December 1916 the Joint Water Board took over the Works and before Christmas all the plant was in the hands of their Inspectors, Messrs. Parker and Revell.

William Underwood retired to Dukinfield but was not destined to see his work completed. The following biographical sketch indicates the impact he made as a Public Works Contractor.

UNDERWOOD OF DUKINFIELD

William Underwood was born at Dukinfield on the Cheshire-Lancashire border, in 1855 and educated at St. Mark's School, which he left at thirteen to work for a local builder and contractor named Jabez Gibson. Before his twentieth birthday William had paid two working visits to the United States and in 1877 he was back at Dukinfield employed by Mr. Gibson as a foreman. 1879, aged 24, William set up in business as a local builder and contractor. His firm prospered and in 1887 he took his step-brother, Mr. G.H. Walker, into partnership. Thereafter the firm was that of William Underwood and Brother. Underwood typified the small town Public Works Contractor whose hard work brought him success and well-earned respect in the neighbourhood.

The firm completed a number of sewerage contracts at Audenshaw, Ashton-under-Lyne, Colwyn Bay, the Monmouthshire Western Valleys (Sirhowy), Ystradmynach in Glamorgan and for the London County Council at Catford Nunhead. In addition to the A. & D.W.B. job Underwood secured several smaller waterworks contracts, with Bury Corporation, the Ashton, Stalybridge and Dukinfield Water Board, the Cawlyd Water Board in the Vale of Conway and finally constructed the small Penderyn Reservoir at Hirwaun, Glamorgan.

Further work carried out by the firm included laying street tramways, as for the Crompton Urban District Tramways near Oldham in 1901. In May 1903 William Underwood & Brother secured the contract for the extension of Colwyn Bay promenade. The firm also built property in Stalybridge, Ashton and Dukinfield, laid out Dukinfield Park and built the artificial lake at Stamford Park, Ashton.

William Underwood was three times elected Mayor of Dukinfield, in 1909/10, 1911/12 and in 1921/22 when he was elevated to the Aldermanic bench. He was appointed J.P. in 1900 and spent thirty years in public life. William served on the Gas, Highways, Parks and Recreation, Finance and Parliamentary Committees of Dukinfield Town Council. He was also a member of Hyde County Council School Board and a Trustee of Ashton Savings Bank. Alderman Underwood was a Governor of the Ashton & District Infirmary and after the war he presented a £1,000 bond to endow a bed in memory of the fallen men of Dukinfield.

For the whole of his life he belonged to St. Mark's Church, where he served as a Church Warden. Just before his death he had completed forty-eight years as a Sunday School teacher. When he died in August 1924 at the age of seventy his name was a household word in Dukinfield. The business died with him and today the name is virtually unknown. His only son, the late Mr. J.W. Underwood, became a solicitor and the King Street firm is still in business under the family name, almost the only link with the past. From a humble beginning William Underwood rose to a position of wealth and eminence which he used in the service of the community. The surviving photographs show him with his period-piece apparatus for constructional work, i.e. his locomotives, steam road roller and chauffeur-driven car.

Step-brother G.H. Walker began life as a bricklayer. He too became prominent in public life serving on the Stalybridge Town Council and as a Cheshire County Magistrate. He died in July 1916 aged 52.

By Direct Labour

Direct labour meant that as from December 1916 the Board intended to complete the work without a contractor. They would recruit the workmen, provide all the extra equipment and meet every contingency that arose. From now on the buck stopped at Newport, it could no longer be passed to Dukinfield.

By 1917 Engineer Jupp was 40 years old and had not gone to War. The Board retained his services and instructed him to prepare for an immediate re-start when the hostilities ceased. This gave the Engineer a breathing space of nearly two years, but there was plenty to be done. At the works he had the problem of the dam foundation to solve and things were still happening at the Village.

In February 1917 the Ministry of Munitions requisitioned the Board's railway for the War Department and ordered the track to be lifted for use at the new Henbury Armaments Factory. An agreement made it clear that the Ministry must replace the railway within six months after the War. Soon twenty men were busy pulling up the rails and by April the track had gone from the reservoir to a point about a mile below the Village. One Spring morning Inspector Parker, living in the huts at Llanfihangel, heard that an officer and fifteen men of the Canadian Forestry Commission had quartered themselves at the canteen and that they were being looked after by Mr. & Mrs. Howard, the stewards.

41

DUKINFIELD at Lower Cwmyoy 1917.

The officer informed Mr. Parker that he had authority from the Home Grown Timber Committee of the Board of Trade to bring timber down the valley by train. He had ordered the track lifting to cease and one mile to be relaid so that the engine DUKINFIELD could be used. It took some time for this news to reach Newport where the Board considered the action to be *"high handed"*: they should have been given proper notice. Meanwhile the soldiers felled the trees and the locomotive hauled them off to Lower Cwmyoy. The tree felling only lasted for a month when fresh orders arrived, the soldiers left and once again track lifting was resumed. Only two more miles had been pulled up when there was another change of plan. The Government had decided to abandon the Henbury factory and the officer in charge of the Explosives Dept., Bristol, wrote to the Board saying that he would not require the rest of the rails.

Reliable witnesses stated emphatically that the track **was not** lifted during the War and equally reliable witnesses said emphatically that it **was** lifted. Both were correct, up to a point, and that point was Ty-hir, four miles below the dam.

Since 1909 there had been numerous changes on the four Urban District Councils and on the Board so, in July 1917, Engineer Jupp presented a thoughtful study of the whole project. Twice he referred to the fact that no powers had been sought for a railway, only for a road. He reminded the Board that the virtually deserted village at Blaen-y-cwm consisted of fifteen huts, a lodging house, a canteen, a shop, police cell, mission room, hospital and surgery, schoolroom and residence. The huts provided accommodation for 200 men but "under new conditions" there would not be room for more than

150 and this number would have to be doubled. He explained that every facility must be increased, except the sale of drink which, he said, *"must be kept down"*. He asked for Dr. Hincks to be re-engaged and for another missioner to be appointed, the latter to be under the authority of the Works Manager. Arrangements must be made with local farmers to bring their produce to the Village and for the pre-war cultural and social services to be resumed. The Blaen-y-cwm social life is still remembered by those who took part enthusiastically in the football and cricket matches, the sports, dances, concert parties, the choral activities etc. but this was part of a carefully thought-out plan. Mr. Jupp remembered that the Underwood navvies drank fiercely — at the Half Moon Inn, Llanthony and at The Globe, Fforest. The Globe was reached easily by train and here the navvies 'stoned' themselves on whisky before *'sleeping it off'* — anywhere. They were quite harmless, it was just a way of life, but the Fforest children became frightened and on occasions the police were summoned to fish navvies out of barns and to pick them up from the lane sides. Mr. Jupp had to extend the railway across the fields to Llanfihangel Station which would give the navvies easy access to Abergavenny. The thought was disturbing and he decided that the best course of action was to develop an interest in the social life, keep the consumption of alcohol down and save the Board's reputation.

An interesting aside on the drink question was that the canteen, being in Breconshire, was legally *'dry'* on Sundays and having a resident policeman the law was enforced. Over the mountain Llanthony was in Monmouthshire, a county then administered as a part of England but also regarded as belonging to Wales. At the Half Moon Inn, Mr. Colley the landlord took full advantage of the confusion and opened on Sundays. The navvies made a good path over the mountain and each weekend they left Blaen-y-cwm as soon as possible. Some went over the top on Saturday afternoon and spent the night at the Half Moon where Mr. Colley provided hospitality in the shape of straw on the stable floor. Others spent their Sundays at the Half Moon and from the opposite hillside at Blaen-y-cwm it was a fine sight to watch the single file of navvies winding their way up the mountain. Their late night return could be heard — if not seen! Mr. Jupp need not have worried too much, for under 'direct labour' and changing social conditions the old fashioned navvy gradually disappeared.

Stories abound, but the post-war lore has nothing like the story of the pre-war navvy who had been 'weekending' at the Half Moon. Returning dazed and sweating, he lay down on the top to sleep it off. Waking in the small hours he found his matted hair frozen to the ground, disentangled himself — and survived.

Transport was still a priority on the Engineer's planning list. A through railway line had never been built, some of the original track had been lifted and the rest of it was in poor condition. Once again the Engineer thought about road haulage but after costing he discovered that this would be twice as expensive as rail travel. The cost of operating a locomotive was only £2.10.0d. a day and one could do the work of several lorries. (This emphasised the serious error of attempting road haulage in 1910). Having decided to use the railway it was necessary to put it in working order and to build a new 1½ mile extension across the fields from Lower Cwmyoy to Llanfihangel Yard. The War Department agreed to pay the Board £8,172 compensation money for their use of the railway.

In November 1917 Mr. Jupp reported that terms had been arranged with the two local landowners, Mr. R. Baker-Gabb and the Vicar of Llanfihangel and also with Abergavenny R.D.C. as the new line would have to cross two public roads.

The two locomotives left on the site were not powerful enough for the traffic so Mr. Jupp said that *"two new specially designed locomotives would have to be bought"*. The Board would also need new engine sheds at Llanfihangel and Grwyne Fawr Works. The railway would be a life line for personnel and a supply line for the Works, which would require thousands of tons of cement and coal as well as provisions.

In addition to the engine shed, the Grwyne Fawr reservoir works would need a new power station, a fully equipped fitting shop, a blacksmith's shop, a carpenter's shop and an office. Under 'direct labour' the Board would now have to arrange for the employment, timekeeping and payment of the workmen.

Speaking about machinery and equipment, Mr. Jupp pointed out that for an average of 3 months a year no masonry work could be done. The Board must therefore obtain the most modern labour saving machinery to compress a year's work into nine months. The equipment needed would include:

A gas engine for suction gas with a generator driving a dynamo.

Two sets of generators.

Equipment at the power station to make the producer gas.

Two stone mason yards, each supplied with electrically driven stone crushing machines capable of crushing 10-12 cubic yards an hour.

A new sand crushing machine to replace Underwood's obsolete apparatus.

A double action concrete hoist to stand 175 ft. high.

An aerial cableway, electrically operated, to span the valley above the reservoir wall. (Length 1,100 ft., maximum height above the ground 250 ft.)

New electric cranes for the reservoir wall working on a 40 ft. radius with a 3-4 ton capacity.

A fresh quarry area would have to be found as Underwood's quarry has been worked to the limit. This would also need new cranes and equipment.

Finally the Works would require air compressors, pneumatic drills and electric light. The village would also need a small power station.

The Board listened to their Engineer with respect, thanked him for a *"thoughtful"* report, agreed to all his proposals and reeled out for tea (or supper).

It was also agreed that a Resident Engineer be appointed to the Works and the Board asked the Army for the release of Captain W.C. Cory Goddard A.M.I.C.E. A.M.I.Mech.E.

The last straw was that time now ran out for the A. & D.W.B. The 1910 Act allowed ten years for completion of the Works so in 1919 there was nothing else for it but to go to Parliament for the third time. The new Act reminded the King's Most Excellent Majesty that owing to *"circumstances arising out of war"* it was necessary to extend the period of construction for another ten years and to grant authority to borrow a further sum of money not exceeding £500,000. The Act received Royal Assent on 4th May 1920. The councillors now faced the possibility of a 20 year construction period and a million pound bill: Oddly the Act allowed 20 years for the completion of the Helyg reservoir though this had been abandoned in 1915. The reservoir was not built and the powers finally lapsed in 1940.

Captain Goddard took up his new duties in January 1919, with Inspector Parker as his second in command. At Llanfihangel the huts had to be cleared of German prisoners of war so that an office staff could be installed until accommodation at Blaen-y-cwm and at Grwyne Fawr Works was ready for them, where the final challenge, the great impounding reservoir, still waited to be built.

From road to rail at Lower Cwmyoy.

45

Travel by Train

C ommunication to the reservoir site was still with an acute problem that early in 1919 the Engineer described the railway as his "Chief Work". The extension line to Llanfihangel Yard was opened on 25th June but on the Lower Cwmyoy to Ty-hir section the track was in poor condition and beyond the latter point there was no railway. In May 1919 the Board took delivery of 575 tons of flat bottomed rail in lengths of 20 ft. and decided to manufacture their own sleepers. As no less than 21,565 were required Tom Pembridge and Bill Harris were kept busy cutting down the oak wood opposite Coed Farm. When Bill Kirby returned to the job with his bride they set out for Blaen-y-cwm by train. Mrs. Kirby had some misgivings about what lay in store for her but Bill's enthusiasm knew no bounds. Unfortunately the railhead was still a mile or so short of the Village and the Kirbys finished the journey pushing their household effects along the road — in a pram.

By September 1919 the rails had once again reached the Village and before the year was out the train was running to the Works. At last the transport problem had been solved and the Board had an eleven mile railway from their yard to Llanfihangel through to the Works.

Engineer Jupp proudly reported that the railway was *"of a very exceptional nature, rising 1,168 ft. in only 10¾ miles"* and that the *"ordinary type of contractor's locomotive was quite unsuitable for such gradients"*. He had drawn up a short specification which had been submitted to six firms "engaged in the manufacture of small locomotives". The Leeds firm of Manning Wardle successfully tendered to supply two new 0-6-0STs by 1st September 1919. They were alleged to be of special design and would cost

£2,975 each. Jupp reported that this was *"twice the pre-war price, but we must have the best"*.

Unfortunately the new engines did not arrive on time but the Ministry of Munitions advertised a 3′0″ gauge 0-4-OT named 'BRIGG' at £1200, with the additional information that this locomotive had just been completely overhauled at Darlington. Said Mr. Jupp *"I therefore had the locomotive inspected at Darlington and after communicating with your Chairman offered the Ministry £1000. They have accepted the offer and promise immediate delivery"*. As the repairs alone had cost £600 this locomotive could be described as *"Brigg the Bargain"*.

Meanwhile the Engineer reported that the ANITA had broken down and that the DUKINFIELD's boiler needed a new firebox. He said that the two new locomotives must be used on the through route, the ANITA repaired and, with the BRIGG, used at the Works. This meant that the DUKINFIELD could be sold. The theory was sound but, as there was still no sign of the new engines, BRIGG was the only machine in working order.

The first Manning Wardle Engine finally arrived at Llanfihangel on 29th April 1920 and was followed by the second on 6th May. They were over six months late and the firm had the usual excuses. There was great rejoicing as Billy Hoffland proudly drove ABERTILLERY No. 1 up the valley with the whistle blowing all the way. The triumph was shortlived. The track was light, the gradients formidable and the heavy locomotives bounced alarmingly. By the end of May both were out of action and the firm was reported to be sending an expert down to Llanfihangel. The outcome was that the rear springs had to be changed, compensating beams fitted to all the spring gear and a five cwt. block of lead bolted to the front end. This kept the engines down on the switchback gradients and took until July 1920 to complete.

These large Manning Wardle locomotives were fine machines and it is difficult to envisage anything much larger on a 3'0" industrial line. The firm had produced a number of similar locomotives so the design was in no way 'special'. The drawings simply came 'out of the cupboard' and they did a 'two-off' job with minor modifications. See Appendix iii.

At last all four locomotives, ABERTILLERY No. 1, ABERTILLERY No. 2, BRIGG and ANITA were at work. Meanwhile the decision was taken to keep the DUKINFIELD. After some bartering Bagnalls undertook to repair the boiler and fit a new firebox for £300. The boiler was removed at Blaen-y-cwm and sent off to Stafford in 1921. It was not returned until July 1922. The Blaen-y-cwm fitters then rebuilt the engine and by October it was once more in service, after a five year rest.

ABERTILLERY NO. 2.

The railway required three engine sheds together with a fitting shop for locomotive and plant repairs. Cwmyoy shed was dismantled in 1920 and a new single road engine shed built at Llanfihangel where a 2,000 gallon water tank was also provided. In June 1920 the existing shed at Blaen-y-cwm was enlarged while at Grwyne Fawr Works a third engine shed and fitting shop was built in 1921; this had to be enlarged in March 1923. At the fitting shops heavy repairs to the locomotives had to be carried out by hand. Wheels and boilers were removed from the frames by means of a hand crane together with block, tackle and packing.

Down at Blaen-y-cwm village the population was steadily increasing towards the 300 mark. Foodstuff, coal and other necessities of life had to be carried up the valley by train as did the vast quantity of Portland cement needed at the Works. The annual returns of merchandise handled at the small G.W.R. Llanfihangel Goods Yard during this period make interesting reading. The figures, exclusive of coal traffic are: 1903 = 116 tons, 1913 = 3,492 tons, 1923 = 4,080 tons and in 1929 = 289 tons. The chaos was considerable.

William Underwood left a number of wagons in the Board's hands, these included four wheeled and eight wheeled bogie side tipping types. In 1920 some new wagons were built at Llanfihangel Yard and in July 1922 the first new 3 ft. gauge coach was built there. In 1923 Messrs. Rowlands supplied 24 side-tipping and three end-tipping wagons. The former cost £13 10s 0d. and the latter £12 10s 0d. each.

At first the workmen travelled from the village to the Works sitting on the sides of the open cement trucks. Later some of the wagons were roofed over, fitted with longitudinal back to back seats and left with open sides. This meant that the men could sit, smoke and chew their baccy with plenty of space to spit into. Later some of the sides where covered leaving the windows unglazed.

Going Home. Period 1922. Engine BRIGG.

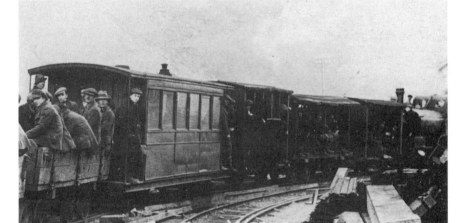

The "pièce de résistance" was the Saloon, or as it was known at Blaen-y-cwm, the glass coach. The Board purchased this vehicle and after repair at Grwyne Fawr the windows were glazed, hence the name. The glass coach was entered from transverse platforms at each end. The glass coach was a 'no baccy' — 'no spitter' reserved for women and children and for special trains carrying visiting officials. It is described in the Appendix iv together with the specially built but little used ambulance coach.

49

A considerable amount of what might be called passenger traffic had to be operated. Each morning and evening the "workmen's mails" carried the men to and from the Works, two miles each way.

The Landladies special at Pont Esgob.

On Tuesdays a "landladies' Special" left the Village at 8.30 a.m. and returned at 4.30 p.m. This allowed the womenfolk to shop at Abergavenny and it usually consisted of the glass coach and a locomotive. The little train made a pretty sight winding its way down the valley. Tuesday was also Dr. Hincks visiting day and he sometimes requested to meet him at Pont Esgob.

On Thursday the cashier, Mr. Frank Hatcher, had to travel to Newport to collect the workmen's wages. He was accompanied by Constable Dew, dressed in civvies and armed with a revolver, as the wages amounted to £1,000 each week. They went by the train to Llanfihangel and then travelled 1st class to Newport where they had a free lunch. The next call was on the Accountant, Mr. Tolson, who supplied the cheque, followed by a visit to the Bank to pick up the money.

Finally there was the Saturday workmen's mail, when worked finished at 12 noon and the train clattered off from the Works to the Village. There was just time for a quick wash and change before leaving again at 1.00 p.m. for

Llanfihangel. In this way some 150 men, women and children were able to spend Saturday afternoon at Abergavenny. The return train arrived at Llanfihangel at 7.0 p.m. and it was a job getting everyone safely transferred from the G.W.R. to the G.F.L.R. The fireman had the task of throwing off any troublesome drunks — who had to walk it back to Blaen-y-cwm. Empty cement trucks were taken down the valley behind the 'mail'. That was no problem, but, when loaded wagons had to be hauled back up the valley — that was! A lot depended on the driver's skill or on his temperament. When steam was in short supply some drivers would stop for a 'blow up' before tackling the next incline. That was playing safe. Another driver, anxious to get home and into the canteen would 'rush' the incline and hope for the best. If the locomotive couldn't make it the passengers were alerted by the sound of the whistle, when they all jumped out and pushed. This often did the trick but if not then the train had to be backed to the bottom of the gradient and steam raised ready for the next attempt.

Sometimes the heavily loaded 'mail' was double headed up the valley from Llanfihangel usually with ANITA piloting ABERTILLERY No. 1. Failure to proceed was not due to the gradients but to lack of steam!

Stanley Edge can remember it all. He was too young to push so they left him on the train for 'safety' — and he had to be content with picking blackberries as the train went slowly past the bushes.

When travelling from the Village to the Works the important people did not ride with the workmen. They preferred to travel with the driver or to stand on the locomotive running plate holding on to the handrails.

The railway was used to supply the Village with milk, most of which came from Farmer Davies of Pen-y-clawdd, Llanfihangel, at 1s 5d a gallon. The train travelled across the farmer's fields and he put the milk churns on a small platform and then helped to fasten them to the front of the locomotive. By the time the train reached the village the milk was well on the way to becoming butter.

The train became a bit too convenient and complaints were received that a man from Abergavenny was using it to *"bring up boots"*, also that a girl was collecting *"meats"* from the farms and using the train to take them to the Village. These commodities were then sold at cut prices which affected trade at the shop. Mr. Jupp decreed that no-one should use the train without holding the Board's permit.

The single line of railway was operated without signals on the "sight and sound" principle of warning. The engines had to be worked hard on the steep inclines and in the quiet valley the train could be heard for several miles.

The journey from Llanfihangel to the Works took one hour with a maximum speed of 20 m.p.h. and an average speed of 12 m.p.h. Remarkably there were no serious accidents on the railway, though the Llwyncelyn farmer once claimed £3.10.0d. *"for a ewe killed by the locomotive".*

51

All the trucks and 'coaches' were loose, coupled by chains with the inevitable snatching and jerking movements. Braking was sometimes effected by putting oak sprags through the carriage wheels in the good old 'wild west' style. Brake power was always a problem. If the train seemed to be getting out of control descending the inclines the locomotive would be put into reverse and given steam. In this way it worked against the load and acted as a brake. More often the steam or hand brake was fully applied but this simply locked the wheels and the engine then slid down the gradient. This resulted in flat tyres, quite a rarity with a railway locomotive.

The weather was always a hazard. Rain and mountain mist made the rails greasy and snow blocked them. At one time a wedge shaped snow pusher was mounted on a bogey and attached to BRIGG in an attempt to clear the drifts. This was not effective and after a blizzard it was a case of 'one out, all out' with the shovels.

In August 1921 the Board's Committee made an official visit to the Works travelling up from Newport by 'chara'. At Llanfihangel they were met by Messrs. Jupp and Goddard, given a good look at Abertillery No. 1 and informed that the machine could haul 15 tons of cement up to the Dam. They were then ushered into the Saloon (glass coach) and en route stopped to see the saw mill in action at Cwm Coed-y-Cerrig where railway sleepers were still being made. They stopped again at Coed Fern Wood (for the same purpose) and later Mr. Jupp informed them that in two places the gradient was 1 in 9! At the reservoir they were shown the construction of the wing gutters. This necessitated diverting the railway towards the 130 ft. long tunnel which would take the track through the base of the wall. Most of the 'progress' noted was with the railway, not the reservoir, a fact which caused some consternation among the councillors. A more relaxed occasion was the visit of the Woolhope Naturalist Field Club in June 1925. They also travelled by train "making a halt at Blaen-y-cwm, 1300 ft. above sea level, to inspect the arrangements made for accommodating the staff and the men of whom there were over 400".

The traffic was so heavy that as early as 1921 it was necessary to relay three miles of track from Pont Esgob to Llanfihangel, where an extra cement shed and sidings were required. These new sidings included a short section of mixed gauge track (3′0″ inside 4′8½″) so that the G.W.R. engine could push wagons to the rail head, and the Board's engine pull them back to the cement transfer shed.

At the other end of the line there were several sidings, inside the reservoir, to reach the stone crushing plant and the spoil bank plus a network of lines at the Quarry.

In September 1923 the locomotive allocations were as follows:

At Grwyne Fawr Works shed BRIGG and DUKINFIELD.

At Blaen-y-cwm ANITA and ABERTILLERY No. 2.

At Llanfihangel ABERTILLERY No. 1.

The engines were maintained in first class condition and Bob Gibson, the foreman fitter, had them painted green with red buffer bars and lined out red, yellow and black.

The following is a list of the engine drivers with the dates when their locomotives were stopped for repair at Grwyne Fawr Works:

ANITA: Drivers Harry Bayliss (Senior), Bill Kirby and Jack O'Hearne. Stopped for repairs in 10/19, 9/21, 7/23 and 2/26.

DUKINFIELD: (Later Abertillery No. 3.) Drivers Joe Williams, Henry Bayliss Senior and Charlie Rawlings. Out of use from 5/17-10/22. Stopped for repairs in 3/25 when the wheels were removed and sent away for new tyres.

BRIGG: Drivers Harry Bayliss Senior and Bill Pattimore. Out of use from 10/22 to 2/23 when new tyres were fitted. Stopped again in 9/23 for new tubes and slide bars, also from 10/24 to 1/25 with a cracked firebox. This repair was not satisfactory and in 11/25 the boiler was removed and sent to Cardiff for repair. The engine was re-assembled at Grwyne Fawr Works in 2/26.

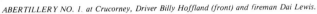
ABERTILLERY NO. 1. at Crucorney, Driver Billy Hoffland (front) and fireman Dai Lewis.

ABERTILLERY NO. 1: Drivers Bill Hoffland with Dai Lewis as his rope runner (fireman) succeeded by driver Holland. No. 1. was stopped for repair as early as 1/23 when the wheels were removed and sent to Leeds for turning. Returned to traffic in 5/23, but stopped again later in the year with a cracked tube plate. In 3/25 the wheels were removed again and sent away for new tyres. In 4/27 described as "having been fully repaired".

ABERTILLERY NO. 2: Drivers Bill Perrin, Wiseman and Bill Kirby. Perrin is remembered as "T.T. and a short tempered man who" got through 18 cleaners in as many months", also as "a marvellous engineman". During 1923 the wheels of this engine were removed and sent away, presumably for new tyres.

Bill Paine of Llanfihangel had charge of the maintenance of the railway and the road. In all there were approximately twenty miles of track which provided employment for two gangs of platelayers.

STANLEY, an old hand of 1880 was not purchased by the Board until 1925. Driver, Arthur Ridout.

The Engineer first requested extra motive power in October 1922 and by May 1925 he reported that this was essential. Two more locomotives arrived in June 1925 and went straight to the Works. They were both O-4-OTs and purchased from Messrs. Adams of Newport, Mon. for £775. STANLEY did not do much work at Grwyne Fawr, being chiefly used on a stream diversion job. MOUNTAIN ASH was a little shunting engine which had received its name on Underwood's contract at Penderyn, where STANLEY had also been at work.

In 1923 someone at Newport attempted a 'time and motion study' on the railway. The theory was as follows — there were only twelve miles of route and five locomotives, yet three engine depots were needed. Why not keep all the locomotives at one central depot? On paper it was a fair question but in practice there would not be any saving because of the light engine working back to the central depot with more overtime pay for the crews. The report reveals that: "locomotive repairs are carried out at the Dam under the supervision of a foreman fitter. When the engines are under repair the drivers act as fitter's mates, some of them are capable of carrying out their own maintenance repairs such as closing up big ends and fitting new brake blocks".

Apparently Trade Unions belonged to the great big world outside the valley. Inspection work was also carried out by the foreman fitter and all the boilers were examined by the Vulcan Company's inspector. The time and motion man was not satisfied so, later in 1923, details of engine working and overtime had to be tabulated for him. The following interesting details then emerged:

ABERTILLERY No. 1, a general purpose locomotive was stabled at Llanfihangel, it worked 12½ hours a day and 7½ on Saturday. The driver and fireman started work at 5.30 a.m. to work the first train up the valley at 6.00 a.m., they also worked the last one down with the empties and post from the Village. The crew stabled the engine and booked off at 6.00 p.m. Mealtime duties were paid. Overtime was worked for the following reasons: breakdown of wagons, running the Saturday mail train, waiting for the doctor and meeting the Works Committee.

ABERTILLERY No. 2 was also a general purpose locomotive, stationed at Blaen-y-cwm and working 13½ hours a day. It was used on the workman's mail morning and night. The crew booked on at 5.00 a.m. and finished at 6.30 p.m. One hour overtime was allowed. This engine was sometimes used on the Route and worked the Saturday mail alternately with No. 1.

ANITA, again a general purpose locomotive, was kept at Blaen-y-cwm shed and worked 13½ hours per day. The engine worked the morning and evening mails with No. 1.

DUKINFIELD was normally stationed at the Dam and the crew worked from 6.00 a.m. to 5.30 p.m. without overtime. When the ANITA was under repair the DUKINFIELD was transferred to Blaen-y-cwm and employed on the workmen's mails.

BRIGG was stabled at the dam and again was worked from 6.00 a.m. to 5.30 p.m. without overtime.

Later the tempo increased as the time for the big push drew near. Bill Kirby would then follow the Llanfihangel engine down the valley with more 'empties' before working a final load back to the Village with overtime. By now no-one was worried about overtime, only about getting the job done, time and motion studies had long since been given up.

BRIGG at the works with driver, pianist Bill Pattimore. Purchased by the board in 1919 from the Ministry of Munitions for £1,000.

The all electric Village

Before the war the isolated house at the head of the valley was just that — home to old Shepherd Charles Morgan, son Lewis and their family. By 1925 the Board had turned the area into a self-contained Village with a population of over 400 men, women and children.

The Board inherited 15 bungalow lodging huts from the Contractor and increased the number to 30. Most of the men who took their wives to the Village turned them into boarding house landladies. For example, Hannah Bayliss, wife of the Black Gang foreman, had one of the larger huts. Their family of six lived at one end with up to 25 lodgers sleeping in a communual bedroom at the other end. *"Mam cooked for her lodgers and scrubbed the bedroom thoroughly each week"*. The men purchased their own food and, fortunately, went home at weekend which relieved "Mam" Bayliss of the washing and ironing. The hard work was not without reward and Harry Bayliss was the proud owner of a bull-nosed Morris car which could be driven safely down the valley — provided the driver knew how to dodge the ends of the railway sleepers. The Board disposed of Underwood's circular 'feet to stove' lodging houses and replaced them with two new buildings. Their double storey hostel could accommodate over 50 men and was managed by Mr. & Mrs. Dean. The carpenter made simple plank beds fitted with straw mattresses. In an 'emergency' a sack filled with bracken was used as a substitute! The second large lodging house was an extended single storey building at the reservoir end of the Village known as 'the shant' and later as 'Extension Villa'. The building could accommodate between 40 and 50 lodgers in two big bedrooms. There was a boiler room for washing and drying and the 'hot plate' room where a huge fireplace, or furnace, heated water in three and five gallon 'fountains'. It also boiled the water in a five gallon steel kettle. Engine Driver Bill Perrin and his wife Emily kept house at the Shant and in addition to the lodgers they had a family of twelve. It was nothing unusual for the Perrins' weekly meat bill to top £20.

One of the officials' houses at the 'posh end' of the village. Inspector Robert and Mrs. Parker with two of their children, Oliver and Myrtle (right), both born at Blaen-y-cwm.

The one-family huts were located at the upstream or 'posh' end of the Village where the Parkers, Edges, Scotts and Hatchers could be found. Strange as it may sound there was some vandalism and the freedom of the 'top end' had to be curtailed. The accommodation included a staff hut for members of the office staff who did not have their wives with them. This was well appointed and included a bedroom for the important folk who had to stay overnight, such as Dr. Hincks and Canon M.E. Davies. During the early 1920's an overnight stay at the Village was quite an experience. The one street (a railway line) was lit with electric lights and by 1923 chief electrician Harry Edge had completed the interior lighting of all the buildings. The outside world still used oil and gas lighting.

The power plant at the Works was D.C. and when work finished the generator was stopped. Accumulators (batteries) supplied power to the Village at night and at the weekends by overhead wires on poles. These followed the course of the railway and can be seen in the photograph.

The canteen, day school, hospital and Mission were all re-opened in 1919 and they became the focal point of Village life.

Mr. & Mrs. Howard returned to the canteen in July. The building was near the railway, on the Grwyne side of the line, and it really came to life at night when men jumped off the bogies (trucks) and into the bar where some remained until 'stop tap'. The canteen contained two bars, a large room, a billiard table, a small room for tradesmen and foremen only with a 'jug and bottle annexe' where the ladies could 'nip in for a quick one'. Women were not allowed at either of the bars.

The walls were decorated with hundreds of postcards and the Social Committee took a special interest in the canteen. In 1922 they went to Newport complaining that the beer was of a poor quality. Ebbw Vale beer was stronger but more cloudy so the Board took no action. Weekday customers had to take it or leave it as about 2000 ft. of mountain separated the canteen from the next local.

There was a certain way of doing things at the 'Blaen-y-cwm licensed canteen and Cork Club'. Rule 4 made it clear that, *"Any member who refuses when challenged to produce his cork, or who cannot produce it shall be fined the sum of £1 free of war duties"*. Only the initiated understood that.

The canteen was the one house with upstairs rooms. In addition to the Howards' living rooms, a large dining-room was available for the use of the Board or other officials from Newport. The Howards were succeeded by Mr. & Mrs. Arthur Holland before brother Ivor and his wife took over the management in 1926. Today Ivor's son Arthur is the Waterworks inspector and he lives at Blaen-y-cwm's only surviving house, the resident Engineer's brick bungalow. Mrs. Elizabeth Holland can remember cooking for the Board, helped by Molly and Gwen Morgan, and the visits of genial Mr. Jupp who enjoyed his food and *"sniffed about the kitchen to see what was on"*.

Next door to the canteen the Board built a large general store for groceries, milk and newspapers. The shop was sometimes referred to as Taylors' 'dry' canteen to distinguish it from Hollands' 'wet' place next door.

Tallyman Joy knocked at every house in the Village. He was a travelling salesman who specialised in clothes, boots and bed linen. Another aptly named character was Mr. Gore, the butcher, who delivered his meat by pony and trap.

The Village drinking water supply came from two tanks on the mountainside, a catchment tank and a filter tank, fed by a pure mountain stream. At a water works village, who would think of anything going wrong? Imagine the surprise when people realised that their water supply began to fail at dinner time and that only a trickle came through the taps for the rest of the day. Bob Parker took Stan Bailey to see if they could trace the blockage. They did. A dead sheep was lying in the feeder stream and diverting the flow of water. During the night enough water soaked through the animal to fill the tanks but when this was drained off they did not refill. Instead of water the villagers were drinking dead sheep soup! Bob and Stan removed the sheep, repaired the fence and decided to say nothing. If the news had leaked out Dr. Hincks would have been kept busy with all sorts of imaginary symptons, but, as it happened, no sickness was reported and for over sixty years the Parker/Bailey secret has been well kept!

Messrs. Vincent Feather returned to the day school, this time with little Vincent. Mrs. Feather was replaced by assistant teacher May Parker. The fourth member of the Feather family was 'Egbert', a three wheeled Morgan car.

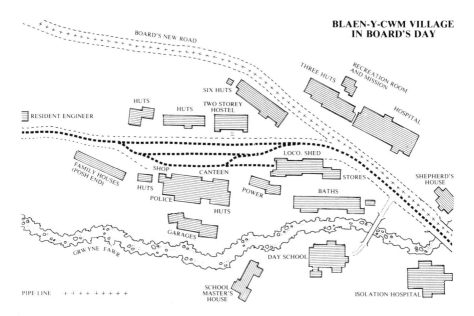

BLAEN-Y-CWM VILLAGE IN BOARD'S DAY

Blaen-y-cwm School was 'co-ed' and comprehensive with two class-rooms, one for the junior mixed and one for the senior mixed. After 1924 the monthly attendance figure exceeded 40 and the highest return was 49 in September 1926. Teaching was sometimes hampered by gales which shook the building and overnight frosts which froze the ink, but in all weathers Constable Dew acted as "whipper in" (attendance officer).

Inspector Parker sent his twin sons, Bill and Tom, to the school, followed later by Len and Olwen. Harry Bayliss 'sent up' George, Bessie, 'young' Harry and Hetty. Ten members of the Ridout family attended — Anne, Ada, Arthur, Bessie, Nellie, Cecilia, Bobby, Joe, Walter and grand-daughter Dorothy. Shepherd Lewis Morgan couldn't believe his good luck in having a school next door to his remote home; Charlie, Gwen, Lil and Johnny just walked up the road to the footbridge and into school. Harry Hatcher was there, with Jacky and Rose Perrin, John, Willie and Vera Scott, Jenny, Roy and Stanley Edge, Ken and Edith Dew — and many another.

Blaen-y-cwm School. Some of the children with the foundation managers. Right to left: Ivor Llewelyn (Head), Inspector Parker, W.C. Cory Goddard (resident engineer), Francis Jupp (engineer) and the two managers appointed by the U.D.C.s'.

After the Feathers had left to take over Pandy Scool, Ivor Llewelyn was appointed head, taking up his duties on 1st February 1923. Stanley Edge wrote from Canada, *"Ivor Llewelyn's tutelage was of such quality that my brother Roy was able to top all Hay 'county' when sitting the Secondary School examination"*. Blaen-y-cwm was Ivor's first headship. From his extant diaries it is possible to see how this passionate idealist committed himself totally to his little school. His main complaint was that once (only) he had to take a fortnight's sick leave. Ivor declined the offer of a headship at a permanent school in Radnorshire and stuck to the temporary school until it had to close at the end of the summer term in 1928.

Dr. Hincks resumed his duties in June 1919 and appointed Sister Thorne to the hospital. She was followed by Sister McKenzie, Nurse Mytton, Sister Whitley and Nurse Williams. Sister Kinsey of Hay also took her turn at Blaen-y-cwm hospital. The isolation hospital was on the left side of the railway just before the bridge over the stream, a site now covered by conifers.

Dr. Hincks normally visited each Tuesday but not so often on horseback now. He had purchased a car which was driven around by a French war widow. The route from Hay to Grwyne Fawr was via Talgarth and Crickhowell to Pont Esgob where Dr. Hincks often left his car and the couple travelled to the Village on the footplate. How long the locomotive and driver were in the siding "waiting for the Doctor" caused little concern at Blaen-y-cwm, but the Newport Committee took note of the fact as a considerable amount of overtime pay was involved. Engine driver Bill Kirby could remember watching the lane for the first sight of the Doctor's car coming down the hill past the Globe Inn.

Tom Hincks hit the national press headlines in 1922. He had treated Mrs. Armstrong, wife of a Hay solicitor, who subsequently died of a mysterious illness. Later the rival Hay solicitor, Mr. Martin, reported sick with similar symptoms. Dr. Hincks' suspicions were aroused when he discovered that Martin's illnesses followed visits to Major Armstrong's house for tea. Everything seemed to depend on whether or not Martin ate Armstrong's home-made cakes. If he didn't he had no symptons. Dr. Hincks decided to notify the Home Office who arranged for Mrs. Armstrong's body to be exhumed. Evidence of arsenic poisoning was immediately visible. Major Armstrong was arrested and charged with murder and attempted murder.

All this was high drama at the Village where Dr. Hincks was so well known and Major Armstrong himself was by no means a stranger. Armstrong made periodic visits to the Works on horseback in the interests of the Rights of the Commoners. At the trial Dr. Hincks and Sister Kinsey, who had nursed Mrs. Armstrong, were key witnesses. Never did the villagers read the 'News of the World' more avidly. The jury found the Major guilty of murder. Major Armstrong was hanged at Gloucester jail on 31st May 1922, the day on which young Harry Bayliss watched the last stone of the railway tunnel lifted into position at the reservoir. The date was inscribed on the stone but it is only visible when the reservoir is empty.

In 1925 Dr. Hincks informed the Board's Committee that his work at the Village had doubled and that he had to spend £100 a year on drugs and dressings against an allowance of only £30.

Fortunately the Village mortuary was not in great demand and it was used for salting down the carcases of pigs! All that remains to remind us of these happenings are the concrete steps that once led up to the hospital door.

After the war the 'Navvy Mission' became the Industrial Christian Fellowship and in 1919 Mr. E.W. Copleston was appointed Missioner. The building was not licensed for baptisms, marriages or confirmations but Holy Communion was celebrated either by Rev. Wyndham Lewis who rode over from Partrishow or by Canon M.E. Davies of Abergavenny.

Romances, weddings and family life added lustre to the proceedings. Lillie Ellis captured Albert Holt's heart and her Sister Edna fell for Charlie Martin. May Parker married Jimmy Boyle, Ada Ridout took on Harry Morgan and Bessie Ridout joined herself to Arthur Trigg. Children followed and soon three generations of Ridouts were in residence. Grandpa 'Bob' and his wife Cecilia came to Blaen-y-cwm in 1912 and remained until the end.

Young men seeking a partner outside the village went down the valley to Tabernacle and Forest Chapels, timing their arrival to meet the farm girls as they left the services.

The Mission and Recreation rooms were joined together so that when the partitions were opened they provided one large dual purpose room. After the Saturday night social the room had to be prepared for Sunday School and Evening Service.

The services were informal and occasionally the harmonium was pushed outside for an open air service. The women sat on the ground while the men stood around bareheaded. Hymns were sung from the Moody and Sankey book and the villagers held their own Harvest Festival. The Missioner prepared candidates for confirmation and some were presented to the Bishop at Partrishow Church.

The Missioner lived next door to his Mission and kept the Village post office and a sweet shop. Mr. Copleston is remembered as a firm man who had to leave in 1921 because of his wife's ill-health. The I.C.F. supplied Mr. Jubb, a more gentle man who left in 1924 when Mr. Saile took over. The latter was a good preacher but a poor postman. He could seldom balance his accounts which had to be sorted out elsewhere.

By Christmas 1925 Harry Edge had completed 5 years at the organ. The congregation, presented him with a complete 'Works of Shakespeare'. This kind gesture illustrates the community spirit at the Village, where the job had become a settled way of life.

The Saturday mail at the village.

The large Recreation Hall contained a stage for concerts, a billiard table, darts, dominoes, cards, etc. Later a wireless and loudspeaker were installed. Dances were held each week with Bill Pattimore at the piano and once a month a dance band from Abergavenny provided the music. Whist-drives were also popular. Bob Gibson organised a Pierrot Troupe, dressed by Mrs. Gibson. They wore black dresses and suits with orange ruffles and trimmings. "Gentleman John" Jones trained and conducted a successful Male Voice Choir, all dressed in dark suits with stiff white shirts and wing collars.

Plenty of outdoor activity was provided. Early in 1920 the Clerk to the Board reported with pride that *"20 allotments had been allocated — and dug"*. The football team played in the Abergavenny and District league and was known locally as the 'Blaen-y-cwm 1st. eleven-very rough'. The village site provided a good training ground, but as there was no playing field the team had to rent a pitch behind Llanfihangel station. It is unlikely that any other team had to travel twelve miles to play a home match. Dick Crowther was a popular captain. The Parker twins, Bill and Tom, Bill Harris and Goalkeeper Pearson played in the early 1920s and are still alive. After a home match the team usually adjourned to the Skirrid Mountain Inn where the landlady warmed their beer in a large saucepan on an open fireplace.

Blaen-y-cwm First Eleven, 1921/22.

The Annual Sports day was held on a piece of flat land below the Village. The occasion required a special train to bring up the spectators, hauled by a neatly decorated locomotive. Then followed the races, jumps, tug o'war, tilt the bucket etc. until everyone was tired out. Commenting on life at the Village, the Argus reporter wrote: *"The people live a happy and contented life on communal lines"*. It is to be hoped that members of the Inspection Committee did not read this paper, but in fact the people lived on railway lines and worked pretty hard.

Sports day special.

Constable 'Bobby' Dew kept everyone in order and, being the 'strong arm of the law' he used it quite freely. Oddly the last thing the 'Bobby' wanted was a court case. The Magistrates' Court was at Talgarth, miles away over the mountain and — there was only one horse. Bobby Dew favoured giving an offender the choice of a 'bashing' from himself instead of prosecution. This choice was occasionally taken and sometimes the policeman got the worst of it! Bob Price refused Bobby Dew's rough justice and he also refused to walk over the mountains. There was nothing for it but to place him in the saddle, handcuffed, and walk to Talgarth via the Rhiw Cwmstabl path.

The lock-up was a concrete building with two cells, covered with corrugated iron. This meant that it looked like the other buildings but wasn't quite so comfortable! P.C. Dew was sensibly tolerant with the drunks either walking the offenders about until they 'sobered up' or locking them up for the night.

The Constable finished his time at the Village and was succeeded by P.C. Richards, a much younger man, but by then the fight was nearly over.

Councillor R.B. Holden must have the last word. At a Board Meeting in Newport he "hoped the huts would not be demolished but that the Village would become a holiday pleasure resort served by (guess what!) — an electric railway"! The Forestry Commission have created a chalet with picnic tables and chairs at the site of the Village but so far there is no sign of the electric railway.

Up at the Works

The road terminated beyond the Village at the Resident Engineer's Bungalow which meant that the final approach to the Works was by rail only. The term 'Grwyne Fawr Works' covered all activities at the reservoir site, two miles above the Village. Before reaching the outside or downstream side of the wall the railway passed between the engine shed, the fitting, blacksmiths' carpenters' and electricians' shops on the right of the line with the power station and offices on the left. Immediately beyond these buildings was Underwood's meter house, before the tunnel through the base of the reservoir took the railway into the area to be flooded. Near the inside or upstream face of the wall stood the tall concrete hoist above which the cableway spanned the valley at a great height. This was referred to as 'the Blondin' after the famous French tightrope walker. The skip could carry a five ton stone and lower it into position on the wall.

The first stone crushing plant and mason's yard was on the right of the railway, which also served a second stonemason's yard en route to the quarry. The Board blasted their stone from the northern extremity of the Works and this quarry was first used in June 1920.

The work-force consisted of a variety of craftsmen and labourers including stonemasons, navvies, the black gang, carpenters and blacksmiths. The majority of whom lived at the Village and commuted by train.

The Stonemasons After quarrying, the stone had to be selected since only top quality material could be used on the wall. This important task fell to Bill Roberts who performed with the aid of a Stetson hat, a cigarette, a piece of chalk and trousers well waterproofed below the knee. He looked every inch a Western cowpuncher. On arrival at the yards the stone was prepared by the 'chippies', as the masons were known.

The wall was constructed of "rough" or undressed washed stone weighing anything from half a ton to four or five tons. These stones were set in a bed of concrete 12 to 15 inches thick. This technique prevented the stones from touching and sealed them into position. These large stones were called 'plums' and the spaces around them were filled with small rough stones, also washed, and known as 'hand plums' because they could be handled by the men. Next a top layer of concrete was added and the process repeated. Dressed stone was only built into the inner and outer faces of the wall.

Cross section of the wall as it neared completion. Note the heavy rough stone 'plums' set in layers of concrete and dressed stone on the outside faces.

At the mason's yard below the wall the stone was loaded on to iron skips and secured to flat rail trucks. These were propelled by the works shunter up to the top of the wall (east side). The skips were removed by the blondin, the stone slung by Arthur the blondin banksman and carried to the wall. The skips were left by the line and the train emptied in this way. 'The empties' were then replaced on the wagons and returned to the yard for another load. The cranes on top of the wall were also used but 'blondin' did most of this work.

The 'chippies' normally worked under cover but in dry weather they worked outside, with the exception of Arthur Hancock who worked outside all the time. 'Affer Ancock', as he described himself, was Inspector Parker's showpiece. 'Affer' lived rough in a roofless cottage below the Village where he slept on sacks. He spent his evenings (drinking Guinness) at the canteen but never missed the train and could always be found chipping away outside, with bare arms while his mates tried to keep warm with such refinements as top coats and scarves.

Some of the masons were Cornishmen who reputedly heard about the job from Inspector Parker, also a Cornishman, and owing to a recession in the trade were glad to find work. At the top yard, foreman Bill Scott, his son John and George Ellis were in charge. At the bottom yard Ned Drew, George Wood and Ted Parkhouse were the foremen.

The Navvies There were five gangs of navvies (or labourers) in charge of 'gangers' Bob Ridout (at the Quarry), Joe Hoffland, Jimmy Holt, Dick Weaver and Joe Neale. Inspector Parker always remembered Mr. Jupp's first visit to the Works. As soon as the officials came in sight, all the navvies stopped work, leant on their shovels and stared at their superiors. This annoyed Mr. Jupp until Bob Parker reassured him, *"It's alright, Sir, as soon as you have gone they will start work again"*. It was just the way the navvy showed his independence.

The Board recruited manpower from the Western Valleys and a number of local people also travelled to the Works each day. This meant that the old-fashioned navvy became rarer and the local labour was always more sophisticated. Stanley Morgan, the shepherd's nephew, was quite honest about it: "We rode to the Works on bogies and only got paid from the time we started work at the dam. There was no pay for being rained off and you know how often that would be up there. The pick and shovel work was done by the traditional navvy who did not care for us miners. We had a different style of work. We used to throw the dirt to the heap but they carried it on the shovel. Between our throws we had a rest but the navvy never stopped. He would either be cleaning his shovel with a sharp edged stick which he carried between his Yorks or filling his pipe with old-fashioned twist. He never had time to stand and stare which was our failure. I used to watch the postman riding over the mountain from Llanthony eagerly waiting to see if he would call at Blaen-y-cwm". (N.B. Yorks were leather straps fastened round the trouser just below the knee).

The workmen's Mess was near the stonemasons' yard and was fitted out with forms and tables. The men were allowed 30 minutes for breakfast and an hour for dinner, reduced to half an hour in the summer. The Mess had a large open fire and a hot plate. In bad weather the fire served a variety of purposes it warmed the cold, dried the wet, boiled the tea water and kept the locomotive sand dry. Outside was the water standpipe and a coaling stage for the busy Works engines.

The Quarry was a bleak and draughty spot and remained a navvy stronghold. The original rock boring method was crude, being done by hand. The drill was

Bill Roberts (stetson) and the quarrymen. The quarry remained a navvy stronghold though local labour was also used as can be seen in the photograph. Compare the navvy on the extreme left of the front row with his counterpart on the right.

driven into the rock by the strikers wielding heavy hammers in rotation while one of the older men held the drill, turning it to ensure a circular hole. Later, pneumatic drills were introduced.

Arthur Trigg was known as a "powder monkey" being one of two such employed on the job. They had charge of the dynamite and detonated the fuse for blasting. The dynamite was stored near the reservoir in two small stone built magazines with concrete roofs, which can still be found tucked away in Cwm Crigws Isaf. After the war it proved very difficult for men to obtain work at Talgarth, Glasbury or Hay and some of them were glad of a job at Grwyne Fawr Works. About 20 travelled over the mountain from Talgarth to work at the Quarry. A few lodged at the Village during the week but as this was an extra expense others made the double journey each day, performing almost incredible feats of endurance. Messrs. Brideswell, Speak, Lloyd and Davies were among those who left home at 4.00 a.m. — for the day shift! The men with cycles would ride or push them to the foot of the mountain and leave them there. Next came the 1000 ft. climb up Rhiw Cwmstabl followed by a two mile mountain track to the Quarry. The shift ended at 5.30 p.m. (payment at 9d an hour) to be followed by a two hour tramp home, though the last few miles would be a downhill cycle ride. Mist, rain and blizzards often made the journey a hazard and sometimes workmen were caught on the mountain ridge, being unable to descend to Talgarth or return to the Works. On one occasion two of them had to spend the whole night on the mountain and all but lost their lives. In winter time, good protective clothing was essential to survival. These men wore thigh length wellingtons with Welsh wool socks, a waterproof mackintosh and cap. Today, a climb from the bottom of the mountain and a walk to the reservoir and back is considered a "good walk", but ten hours work at the Quarry would kill most of us.

The east side rock fault of 1927. Men about to be lowered 70ft to pump concrete into the cracks.

The Black Gang They were the men with dirty jobs. They maintained all the machinery at the Works, which required considerable skill and ingenuity. One of their first jobs was to erect the concrete hoist, section by section until it towered 200 ft. above the ground. Above the hoist was the 'Blondin' cableway and some maintenance work had to be carried out from the skips at a dizzy height. The men employed in the Black Gang were fitters and turners and their mates, also the engine drivers, the crane drivers and their firemen, all under foreman Harry Bayliss. Bob Gibson was the foreman fitter and his shop was equipped with three lathes, two drilling machines, a shaping machine and hydraulic press, all belt driven from the countershaft of a vertical steam engine.

The power station contained two Rushton Hornsby 250 h.p. twin cylinder gas engines and an Ingersoll Rand air compressor. All the electrical power and lighting at the Works, and down at the Village was under the supervision of Chief Electrician Harry Edge assisted by Bert Walkey and Dick Crowther.

By August 1921 over 200 men were employed at Grwyne Fawr Works, and the wages bill was £800 a week. Both figures would have to increase. In the eyes of some councillors progress seemed to be very slow. "All this great expense", exclaimed one of them, "and the wall is not yet 30 ft. above the ground".

The contrast between the working conditions in the Newport Boardroom and those at the Works was sometimes overlooked. On one occasion a wet 24 hours in the mountains produced 2½ inches of rain when 58 million gallons of water poured off the hills, flooding the Works and washing away a 60 feet long railway bridge near the masons' yards. The Black Gang had to restore everything to working order and rebuild the bridge "in a more substantial manner".

Carpenters, Blacksmiths and others. Eddie Hawkins served under Captain Goddard in the Royal Engineers and later became foreman carpenter at the Works. His shop was always busy and as late as May 1924 the Board had to open up a new wagon works. A number of cement wagons and all the "passenger coaches" were built by the joiners using wheels and axles left behind by the contractor.

Edgar Ellis, a "well paid and jolly man", was the foreman blacksmith and such was the demand made on his department that a "new power operated forge" had to be installed in July 1923.

Bill Bowen the weatherman is a well remembered character. Bill was not concerned with weather forecasts. He had to measure the water flow at the two weirs, the one above the Works near the Quarry and the other below the intake valves. In this way, the Works' water consumption could be calculated, an essential task as Lord Glanusk had to be paid for it. It was also necessary to monitor the outflow downstream to supply the farmers and others. This figure had to be reported to the person responsible for attending to the "rights of the commoners". Bill also walked the mountainsides each day reading the rain gauges. These figures had to be reported at the office and sent to Mr. Jupp at Newport. Each week Bill removed the chart from the hyetograph (an instrument for charting or mapping rainfall) which was located at a point higher than any other in the British Isles. Finally, once a fortnight he had to visit the rain gauges located in the outlying sections of the watershed. On one occasion Bill did not return from his long distance tramp and a search party was sent after him. They went first towards dangerous Bishops Rocks above Capel-y-ffin but found that the rain gauges beyond this point had been read. At the end of the day there was no trace of Bill. A mist had forced the weatherman off the mountains and he finally sought refuge at Dr. Hincks' home in Hay. (See footnote). Though no lives were lost through exposure, three men died as a result of injuries sustained at Grwyne Fawr Works.

Outstanding in the memories of all employed 'up at the Works' was the continuous rain and intense cold. It was the outdoor labourer who suffered most, particularly if not reared in the navvy tradition. Many of the men came straight from the trenches and wore Army puttees around their legs. Sometimes, at the end of a day's work, they had to break off the ice before these could be unwrapped. At £3 a week the wage appeared quite good — unless it was wet. The stonemasons, carpenters, blacksmiths and members of the Black Gang could work under cover while the outdoor worker was laid off without pay. They often had to sit in the cabin with wet clothes and on occasions did not earn enough money to pay their lodging charge. Judged by present day standards those of fifty years ago are almost unbelievable.

Steam crane working at the quarry end of the reservoir and loading stone for building the dam wall.

View from the Reservoir wall, 28th March 1928.

FOOTNOTE: The Grwyne Fawr rainfall and stream gauges were located at the following points: Above Tarren-yr-Esgob at 2122 ft. above sea level, at Twyn Tal-y-Cefn (2303 ft), at Blaen Grwyne Fawr (2200 ft.) at Pen-y-Manllwyn (2500 ft.) and at Waun Fach (2660 ft.) Starting from the Dam Site a round tour of these summits involved a climb of over 1000 ft. and walking seven or eight miles. In addition there were rain gauges at the reservoir, nearby at Aber Clyd and in Cwm Grigws Uchaf.

Nil desperandum (1926-28)

In June 1926 an alarm was sounded. The Finance Committee let it be known that the final cost of the project would be approximately £1,000,000 and that seventy years would now be required to repay the sums of money loaned to the Board. This ten year extension of time necessitated the fourth Abertillery and District Water Board Act of Parliament which received Royal Assent on 8th July 1926 and the Welsh Water Authority is still paying the Bill! The new Act contained 22 clauses mostly referring to the rates, charges and maintenance of the water supply. The final clause was the clearest: *"All costs and charges relating to this Act to be borne by the Board . . . ."*, which meant the bill for these four Acts of Parliament totalled approximately £20,000.

There was a good deal of work yet to be done. Of the sixteen overflow bays only eleven were finished. The valve tower had to be completed and at the bottom of the wall there was the railway tunnel to be filled in. This latter job would take at least two months. There was one gleam in the gloom. Some men were reported "clearing and levelling" a site at Llanfihangel Yard to store plant no longer required at the Works. This pleased the harassed committee. In November the administration was divided into three main committees in an attempt to increase efficiency:

1. The Stores and Canteen Committee.
2. The Works Committee.
3. The Finance Committee.

The dam wall nearing completion. Note the two tunnels for the trains and to carry Underwoods' main through which the water flowed after April 1915.

In 1927 the Minute Books record that "the Committee must be on the site to boost the morale of the men". It was considered wiser to spend the odd £10 on travelling expenses than to contemplate dragging on into 1929 at something like £600 per week. In July 1927 there was "a desperate need to finish before the winter slows down the work. We must make an all-out effort with the maximum number of men. The job is now costing £10,000 a month — the work must be completed this summer so that the dam can be filled up during the winter". All essential work was completed during the summer of 1927 when 450 men were employed at the Works.

In November 1926 the engineer had reported the need for a "new road" to give access to the top of the dam so that the tunnel could be filled in and material routed above the reservoir. This would necessitate a new bridge over the stream near the fitting shops. The "new road" was a railway line laid up the hillside to 1,670 ft. This third section of railway was reported unfinished in April 1927 and in July the tunnel was still in use. Meanwhile machinery from the quarry and from the stonemason's yard was removed through the tunnel. When this was no longer available equipment was lifted over the wall by crane because the steep gradient on the new extension railway made the descent dangerous. Late in August the Works Committee reported that the railway to the top of the dam was complete and on 1st September 1927 a party travelled to the summit by the high level line. The train stopped near the fitting shops, reversed over the bridge and pushed the carriages up the half mile incline to the level of the new roadway. Here it reversed again and went forward towards the quarry. In doing so the train crossed the 1,800 ft. contour line, the highest altitude reached by an adhesion-worked railway locomotive in the British Isles.

The Board's desperate need to finish the job was matched by the desperate need of many people to find work. In 1926 47 couples applied for the job of steward and stewardess at the hostel. Seventy-six men were laid off in July 1927 and two members of the staff had already left. 100 more were due to go but still 357 were employed on the job. By October 1927 all the overflow bays and the valve tower had been completed. Progress was now hampered by an unexpected fault in the rock on the east side, first reported in November 1926. It required a 70 ft. deep excavation to clear and kept the Committee's nerves on edge in 1927.

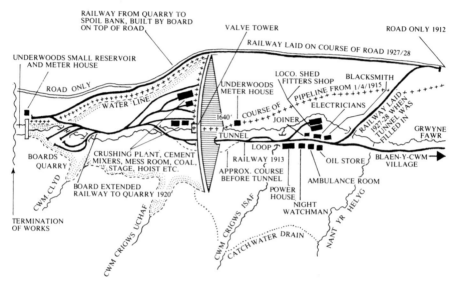

LAYOUT AT QUARRY & RESERVOIR

By now the motor age was catching up with Blaen-y-cwm. At weekends the Saturday mail was rivalled by colliery buses to Nantyglo and Abertillery. Four vehicles operated for the benefit of those going home for the weekend but the "regulars" remained faithful to the train.

The valves were closed on 10th February 1928 and a fortnight later the water was 50ft. above the culvert. All was reported to be in order and the opening ceremony was fixed for the 28th March 1928. The great day was at last in sight.

At the fitting shops Bill Parker's last job was to turn the brass top for the flag pole above the valve tower. The Board's flag would soon be proudly fluttering over the completed works. In February and March every one was busy finishing off everything as the water continued to rise. Two decades had passed since Baldwin Latham 'discovered' the Grwyne Fawr stream back in 1906 and since the County Water Bill had been defeated in the Parliamentary Session of 1908. Death had taken its toll. Latham and Underwood had by now joined the great majority as had many former members of the Water Board.

76

Was there a member of the original 1910 Committee still serving and able to travel to the site on 28th March? Only one, Councillor David Lewis J.P. To him fell the honour of opening the reservoir. Amongst the officials in the party who had their photograph taken at the farm in February 1912 a number had seen the job through, including Francis Jupp and the Tolsons.

The great day arrived and the Grwyne Fawr Light Railway prepared to carry its heaviest ever passenger traffic. Between 300 and 400 people travelled to the top of the reservoir in two trains. Jupp had something to worry about, remembering the three men killed on the construction and many a railway wagon rolling over and over down the spoil bank. The thought of passenger trains zigzagging their way to 1,800 ft. was alarming. They also had to descend. Fortunately, the Daily Sketch photographer was there to record the event. The passengers were not nimble-footed employees, but gentlefolk with pinstripe trousers, spats and fur coats. The party included Judge L.C. Thomas, Major Cheeseman, their Worships the Mayor and Mayoress of Abergavenny, Professor G. Knox, Captain Vaughan Williams and the Vicar of Abergavenny. Locomotives Nos. 1 and 2 were polished up in readiness. As the guests arrived another novelty was revealed. On this day the G.F.L.R. had a printed timetable, its first and last, which read as follows:

11.00 a.m.	Trains leave Llanfihangel Depot.
12 noon	Arrive Blaen-y-cwm village.
12.15 p.m.	Light refreshments.
1.30 p.m.	Leave the village by train for the reservoir top.
2.00 p.m.	Arrive at the reservoir.
2.30 p.m.	Councillor D. Thomas, Chairman of the Board to present Councillor D. Lewis J.P. with a key to open the valve tower. The opening ceremony and dedication. Miss Heather Stuart Tolson to present a bouquet to Mrs. David Lewis. Inspection of the valve tower and reservoir.
3.15 p.m.	Trains leave the reservoir top for Blaen-y-cwm.
3.45 p.m.	Arrive at the village.
4.15 p.m.	Depart from the village.
5.15 p.m.	Arrive at Llanfihangel depot.

Notes. For "those bringing private cars the route on the outward journey will be via Usk, Abergavenny and thence along the main Hereford road to Llanfihangel Crucorney where AA scouts and/or signs will indicate the route to Blaen-y-cwm. A special parking place will be provided for cars at the village. Those desirous of proceeding to Blaen-y-cwm by the Board's light railway should park their cars at Llanfihangel depot".

Opening day special leaving Llanfihangel Yard, 28th March, 1928.

It must have been some rally. Certainly travelling alongside the railway by car and bumping over the sleeper ends for about seven miles would have been more than an adventure. All the party had to travel from the Village to the reservoir by train over the really dangerous section of the line, all except one that is. They were doing what no member of the public had ever done before or would ever do in the future. The only hitch was a derailed coach which was left behind. The event caused some scrambling for fresh places. Doctor Hincks did not have a case of hysteria and the Vicar dedicated the reservoir "To the Glory of God and the service of His children for ever". A number of visitors climbed over the mountains from Talgarth and Hay to attend the ceremony and the employees had their own celebration dinner in the canteen. Blaen-y-cwm had never seen so many hats, spats, flags and furs.

The tales surrounding the opening day are many but only the stories told over and over again can be accepted. An hour of 'light refreshment' in the canteen made one councillor light in the head. He informed his colleagues that "he was not going up there by train". They sent him up the mountain road from the Village by foot and he missed the opening ceremony. After the event a man was found lying in the road with his face on the cylinder block of his motor cycle and badly burned. By then Dr. Hincks was well on the way to Abergavenny Town Hall where the 6.00 p.m. morning dress dinner brought the celebrations to a climax. The programme included ten toasts, two solos, two vocal selections and a quartet finale. Employees at Newport listened with amazement to their colleague's description of the function, which prompted one of them to write, *"Today few can remember what an orgy it was — I'm glad I missed it — the dust didn't settle for years".*

78

Gone to Lion City

At the end of his life Oliver Cromwell remarked, "It is not my business now to eat or drink but to make what haste I can to be gone". After the 28th March 1928 there was little else for the Blaen-y-cwm people to do but to make what haste they could to be gone, taking the machinery and the railway with them. The end had come at last for quarrymen, stonemasons, labourers, fitters and their mates, roperunners, engineers, landladies, the policeman, the schoolmaster and children, the shopkeepers, canteen stewards, doctor, nurses and missioner. Before performing the last rites it is necessary to include a brief description of the Works which remain as an abiding monument to creative genius and human skills that had at last brought the Abertillery and District Water Board to fruition.

The following account is taken from the inauguration booklet written by Chief Engineer J. Francis Jupp M. Inst. C.E.

"The Grwyne Fawr reservoir has a top water level of 1,790 feet above ordnance datum. The height enables a gravity fed supply of water to be given to any point of the Board's district, the draw-off levels varying from 1,150 feet at Abertillery to 200 feet above sea level at Risca. The capacity of the reservoir is approximately 400 million gallons. The effective height from the culvert outlet at the base to the overflow weir at the top is 151 ft. The roadway is 5 ft. above the weir level and the foundation of the dam is 17 ft. below the culvert,

giving a total height from the foundation to the roadway of 173 feet. The
extreme length of the dam is 918 feet and the length of the top water level 655
feet. The thickness of the base is 130 ft., the top width 15 ft. with a 10 ft.
roadway across. The quantity of masonry used is equal to a weight of
approximately 207,000 tons". Over 16,000 tons of Portland Cement was
transported to the site by train. The stone is the old red sandstone quarried
from the mountain. Referring to the Brecon Beacons and the Black Mountains
Sir R. Murchison wrote: *"In no other tract of the world which I have visited is*
there seen such a mass of red rock, estimated at a thickness of 8,000 to 10,000
ft., so clearly inter-collated between the Silurian and the carboniferous
strata". In places the reservoir is built into the mountainside as much as 30 ft.
Liquid cement was forced by compressed air through tubes up to 40 ft. in
length to fill up the cracks in the rock and prevent leakage. The dam wall is
constructed on a curve of 2,500 ft. radius; 16 overflow arches are provided to
carry the roadway and give a total length of 160 ft. for the overflow weir.

The water is taken from the reservoir by means of five 15" diameter draw-off
pipes with copper roses spaced 25 ft. apart (fitments of a mesh type which act
as a sieve to prevent large debris entering the pipes). These pass into a shaft
containing the controlling valves actuated by geared headstocks in the valve
house at the top of the dam. The water is admitted to a 15" diameter vertical
standpipe which connects to the supply main in the outlet culvert. "Owing to
the exceptional purity of the water no filtration is necessary but fine copper
mesh screens are provided immediately below the reservoir". The supply main
to the district consists of a steel pipe 16" in diameter having a total length of 22
miles from the reservoir to Cwmtillery. The main leaves the reservoir at 1,637
ft. above sea level and joins the new road at 1,590 ft. It will be remembered
that Work No. 8 continued this mountainside road past the reservoir, joining
the old track which came up through the ravine. The main is below the road
down to Blaen-y-cwm village and continues below it to Fforest, thence over the
high ground near the Sugar Loaf Mountain and across the Usk to Cwmtillery
service reservoir. From here a steel main of 12" diameter and 11½ miles in
length passes through the Board's District to Nantydraenog Reservoir near
Mynyddislwyn Church.

In order to meet the cost of their water supply the inhabitants of the district
had to face a water rate of 2/-d. in the £ to be paid within the 70 year time limit
imposed by Parliament. The supply main is now worked to full capacity. Two
million gallons a day are fed to the district, 250 thousand gallons a day are
drawn off to supply other sources and 750 thousand gallons a day are allowed
to flow down the stream. Thus the daily outflow is three million gallons or
over one thousand million gallons a year. Meanwhile the reservoir continued
to fill and the high level water mark was reached for the first time on 25th
November 1928.

Notices of the impending sale of plant appeared in "The Engineer" as early as
October 1927 and by the 2nd May 1928 £2,084 worth of equipment had
already been disposed of in addition to the stone crushing plant which went to
Messrs. Pugsley of Bristol for £700 on the 18th February. This firm and that of
Messrs. Le Hane McKenzie & Shand were the chief purchasers, particularly
the latter firm which bought £2,450 worth of equipment in May and June

Blaen-y-cwm Village, period 1925.

1928. The Bristol firm paid £3,300 for four locomotives, the railway track, concrete hoist and scrap metal. Local farmers bought the carriages for use as storerooms or chicken pens and the railway sleepers can still be found serving as gate posts. The sale of plant realised over £12,000 which Councillors T.H. Mytton and D. Lewis "considered very satisfactory".

By the end of the year the Village had almost disappeared. The canteen was sold to the Hope Baptist Church, Cross Keys, for use as a schoolroom. A widow purchased the schoolmaster's house and had this re-erected opposite the beautiful Church of Llanbedr in the adjacent Grwyne Fechan valley. The horrified Churchwarden offered her more than the value of the building just to take it away, to no avail, and there it remained until 1974. As planning permission for a replacement house could not be obtained the owner decided to encase the building with pre-cast concrete blocks and reglaze it. The building is now much more attractive.

The 'Blondin' towers were hauled down the railway and cut up for disposal at Llwyncelyn. Finally the Kirbys moved to the empty corn miller's cottage at Pont Esgob to complete the track lifting.

Locomotives Abertillery No. 1 and No. 2 remained at Llanfihangel until February 1929 when they were sold and sent to Bristol for overhaul. They were then shipped to Singapore and put to work on a Malayan reservoir site that was to supply water to Lion City. By 1934 they had moved again and Ron Copleston, son of the Missioner, noticed them in the Kowloon area of Hong Kong. (See Appendix: Locomotive history).

ABERTILLERY No. 2 had been the last engine in steam to complete the track lifting. Early in 1929 the Grwyne Fawr Light Railway was no more. In October the Board ordered the land formerly occupied by the railway between their depot at Lower Cwmyoy and Llanfihangel Yard to be restored to the farmers and land-owners. So it was that during the winter of 1929/30 the work of removing fences, filling gaps, fitting gates, levelling down and generally making good this section was completed. On the 14th June 1930 a newspaper reporter revisited the works and wrote that "the railway is gone". Everything else went with it. The Board demolished the Village at Blaen-y-cwm and the Works at the reservoir site. Today there is no sign of ugly iron or pipework above ground. With a thoroughness that would have delighted the conservationist, they took their "litter" with them, leaving behind only the water and a fine public road into the hills. The surface of the road is maintained by the respective County Councils and the walls and foundations are repaired by the Welsh Water Authority. The small embankment across the last field at Lower Cwmyoy remained in position until the 1950's and divided this field into two. By this time modern farming methods made it necessary to dispense with the barrier. Farmer Bevan of Stanton Manor remembers the removal, which cost his father £50.

At Blaen-y-cwm Shepherd Lewis Morgan saw it all come and go, no doubt with mixed feelings. He was once knocked over by a locomotive but not seriously hurt. Mrs. Morgan used to walk the fifteen miles to Abergavenny market carrying two baskets of eggs. She sold them and then walked home. Later the 'landladies special' train was a help but she finally succumbed to the luxury of a motor-cycle pillion seat. The Shepherd died in 1929 and the family left Blaen-y-cwm in 1938 but John Morgan still tends his sheep near Blaen-y-cwm.

The last family house at the 'posh end' of the Village was the one built for Mr. Hatcher and his family. This was not demolished and the Hollands lived there until 1962 when the former Engineer's bungalow was made into two houses. The 'Hatcher house' was then demolished and the concrete police cells were also removed in 1962.

John Francis Jupp was a Brighton man who came to the area in 1905 to take charge of the Western Valleys Sewerage Scheme. He was appointed Surveyor to the Board in 1911 and retired in 1935. Mr. Jupp was a member of the Institute of Civil Engineers and remembered as a conscientious kindly man. He made periodic visits to the Dam in a chauffeur driven car but was nervous on top of the wall. He was also nervous in the car when it was driven beside the railway and rode with one hand on the door handle ready to jump! He died in 1942. Mr. Cory Goddard returned to the Board to succeed Mr. Jupp as Chief Engineer, until his semi-retirement in 1949. He remained in office until his death in 1957.

Inspector Parker was a stalwart who served the Board faithfully. A Cornish stonemason by trade, he had previously worked at the Elan Valley waterworks. Lord Glanusk made him the river keeper with authority to fish himself, to allow a limited number of other fishermen to enjoy the sport and to prevent illegal fishing. Mr. Walter Baker-Gabb also gave Bob Parker shooting rights in the hills, a couple of rare privileges. He retired in 1934.

After 1928 the Board could enjoy the Water Works they had struggled so hard to complete. Business became more or less routine until the Second War when 'Dad's Army' looked after the reservoir. In June 1951 there was further talk of expansion owing to a predicted shortage of water in 1970. Engineer Goddard surveyed the Llanthony Valley with a view to flooding it, but the work was delayed because of the "great expense". Strangely there was no mention of reviving the Helyg reservoir scheme of 1914. 1970 saw the end of the Abertillery & District Water Board. On April 1st it was amalgamated with other water works in the County of Monmouth to form the Gwent Water Board. Four years later the Board was merged into the Welsh National Water Development Authority, now more simply called the Welsh Water Authority.

Throughout its separate existence the Board had four engineers, Messrs. B. Latham, F.J. Jupp, W.C. Goddard and P. Beard. Similarly the Clerks to the Board were Messrs. T.S. Edwards, A.G. Edwards, N.C. Moses and S. George.

The predicted water shortage became a reality in 1976. Low rain fall during the preceding two years reduced the level and the 1976 drought emptied the reservoir. The sun baked banks and base looked like a 'set piece' in Arizona, a sight not seen before or since. The official description was, "Water capacity down to 1%".

It was anticipated that some years would pass before the high water level was restored, but so heavy were the autumn rains that before the end of the year water was again pouring through the overflow bays and 1976 had an average rainfall!

Wordsworth loved water. In a sonnet about a favourite river he concluded:

"While we, the brave, the mighty and the wise, we men,
Who in the morn of youth defied the elements, must vanish, be it so!
Enough, if something from our hands have power
To live, to act, and serve the future hour
And if, as toward the silent tomb we go,
Through love, through hope and faith's transcendent dower
We feel that we are greater than we know".

In June 1970 Bill Kirby travelled to the top of the dam for the last time. I jokingly reminded him that we did not have a permit for the visit. Bill replied with a powerful phrase . . . In thought he was somewhere down below, back in the 1920s and driving his locomotive up to the Works. A tendency to exaggerate only made his reminiscences more interesting. Bill died at the end of 1971 and had requested to be buried in Llanfihangel Churchyard within sight of the Black Mountains. So he is.

"Enough, if something from our hand has power to live, to act, to serve the future hour".

APPENDICES

i THE ROUTE

The Route was a term used to describe the communication from the yard near the main line to the site of the works. Its complexity in this case can be gauged from the following analysis:

i) Llanfihangel yard to Lower Cwmyoy. A railway across the fields, 1½ miles.

ii) Lower Cwmyoy to Pont Esgob. A new road with a railway subsequently laid on its surface. Three passing places for road and rail traffic, 1¾ miles.

iii) Pont Esgob to Blaen-y-cwm village. The course of the main pipeline to Abertillery. The original road surface of 1912 above the pipeline with a railway laid on it in 1913. Crossing places for road and rail traffic at ½ mile intervals. Length 6 miles.

iv) Blaen-y-cwm village to the reservoir. (a) The new public road along the hillside to the reservoir top and quarry. One passing place for road traffic only. (b) The railway along the valley bottom to the reservoir site and quarry. Length 2½ miles.

v) A short section of railway from a junction near the fitting shops at Grwyne Fawr and up the hillside to the level of the road at iv (a) above and to the site of the reservoir and quarry. Total 11-12 route miles.

Llanfihangel to Lower Cwmyoy. The name Llanfihangel Crucorney means the Church of St. Michael at the corner of the rock. The rock is the nearby Skirrid Fawr or Holy Mountain, the silent observer of all things local. The summit can be reached quite easily to reveal the outline of the Black Mountain range. St. Michael's Church is medieval with an Elizabethan tithe barn nearby. In the 1920s, Vicar Hughes exchanged his horse for a motor-bike but hay is still in the tithe barn stable. A piece of Church "treasure" which is never on the inventory is a small photograph of Mr. Hughes and his sister seated in a workman's coach attached to ABERTILLERY No. 1. It was taken outside the engine shed in 1922. Bill Harris played football for Blaen-y-cwm and still lives at Llanfihangel. Nearby is the Court, basically a Tudor house which reputedly gave hospitality to Charles I. The Skirrid Mountain Inn has a cobbled forecourt and a horse-mounting block.

Travelling towards Abergavenny, turn right on to the old Hereford road which crosses the main railway line about half a mile from the village. Take the view from the left parapet of this bridge. In the distance is the Holy Mountain, in the immediate foreground a small white cottage. This was Mr. R.H. Baker-Gabb's private waiting-room built for his shooting-party guests en route to Coed Dias where Mr. Baker-Gabb was Lord of the Manor. He died in 1918 and the waiting-room was sold. Steps descended to the down main line platform. Llanfihangel station had "staggered" platforms on each side of the road bridge with a wooden crossing at rail level. Trains pounded up the inclines giving travellers ample warning of their approach. Banking engines were often needed on the 1 in 82/95 gradient from Abergavenny, dropping off the trains at the station. To the right is the site of the up refuge siding and two more sidings which formed the small goods yard. One of the latter was extended to the clump of trees at the far end of the yard where it made connection with the Board's light railway. In the background is the Bryn Arw Hill, beautifully green in the summer months and more lovely still when the bracken turns gold in the autumn or when lightly covered with snow. Llanfihangel station closed in 1958, and only the station-master's house remains.

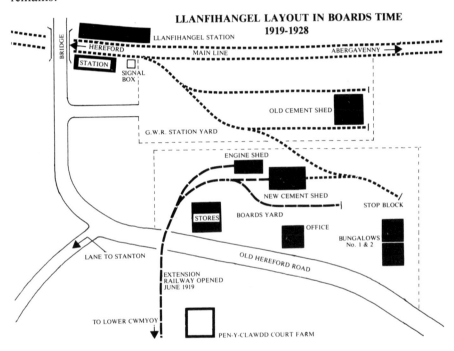

LLANFIHANGEL LAYOUT IN BOARDS TIME
1919-1928

Nearby, the lane from Stanton farm comes in on the right and was Underwood's traction engine route to Lower Cwmyoy. On the left, one of the Blaen-y-cwm huts still serves as a bungalow. Brick bungalows and modern houses now occupy the site of the Board's yard. There were two cement sheds, two bungalows, a stores, an office and a crane. Near the GWR boundary fence a siding led into the engine shed that housed ABERTILLERY No. 1 from 1920-28. The yard was a busy little place and required a one man night shift. Fred Lloyd combined the office of engine cleaner, 'lighter up' and night watchman. After 1928 the Board's cement shed became a warehouse and the area was known as Warehouse and Yard. In 1971 this warehouse was demolished and the site developed as a residential district, now St. David's Close!

In order to obtain the best view of the local railway tracks, travel to the hamlet of Pant-y-Gelly where the traction engine bound for Pont Esgob turned in the hollow before attempting the ascent to Bettws. Stop at Chapel farm, Bettws, and climb the hill. On the Llanfihangel side the descent is steep, giving an aerial view of the course of the tramroad, the main line railway and the route of 1919.

Returning to Llanfihangel, the Board's wooden buffer stops are still in position to mark the railhead. There are four of them, two 3 ft. gauge posts inside two 4′ 8½″ gauge. The alignment here is alongside the course of the tramroad. Leaving the yard the route passes through the housing area and crosses the old Hereford road. This crossing was protected by gates.

The Route climbs gently towards the Llanthony Valley with Bryn Arw on the left blocking the way to Gwryne Fawr Valley, and Pen-y-clawdd Court farm comes into view. This lovely old manor house dates from the 15th century. It has ancient oak timbers and the remains of a double moat defence work. Two pieces of railway rolling stock survive at the Farm, one being the Ambulance coach (See Appendix i). Still rising, the Route passes through a very shallow cutting in the field made to keep the level, not because of the gradient. Soon the descent to Stanton begins. Beyond Pen-y-clawdd fields the course is not easy to follow as the land has been ploughed, though it can be traced alongside the hedges. Near Stanton Manor farm several field gates open into an access lane along which the railway travelled. Here sleepers have been left embedded in the ground. The course of the Route is clear until this access lane joins the old track from Stanton to Fforest. This was replaced by the Board's new road in 1912. Three fields separate this track from the Route at Lower Cwmyoy and all trace of the railway has been removed from them. The lane was gated for the railway as there was little road traffic after 1912. Follow the track or lane through Stanton Manor farm, bear left on to the Llanthony Road (B.4423) and in a few yards turn left again on to the Route. Here was located the 1913 railhead and beyond is the site of Lower Cwmyoy depot, now identified by the roadside clearing used for grit. The place is of considerable interest. Looking across the field towards Skirrid Fawr the far side reveals just a trace of the small embankment that brought the railway across this last field. The depot had little significance after it ceased to be a railhead.

It was here that William Underwood & Brother, together with Manager Messam, began their three-pronged attack on the Grwyne Fawr Valley in February 1912. They tackled the new road from Lower Cwmyoy and from Pont Esgob simultaneously. They also sent their pack horses over the mountain road to Blaen-y-cwm. The first sod was cut in the field below Llwyncelyn farm and the officials were photographed nearby. The farm building dates from the 16th century.

The mountain road to Blaen-y-cwm, approximately seven miles from Lower Cwmyoy. Follow the Llanthony road for a short distance to the Queen's Head Inn and turn left up the hillside. A long climb leads to a gate and on to the mountainside below Twyn-y-Gaer summit. This was formerly an iron age settlement and has been excavated. The mountain road continues towards a

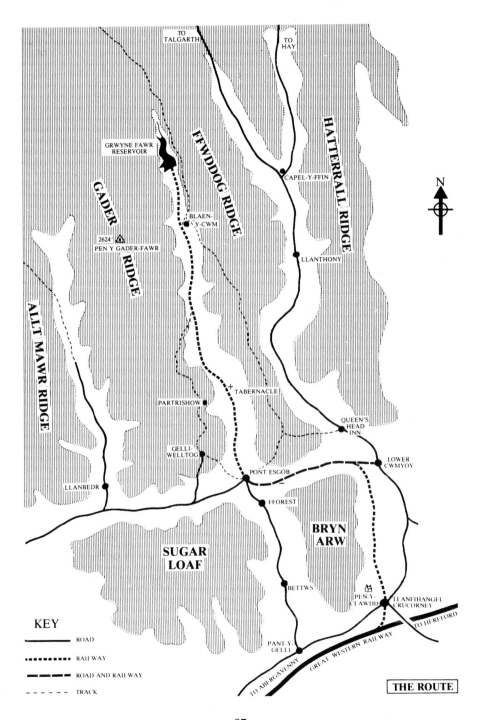

N

KEY

————————	ROAD
••••••••••	RAILWAY
— — — — —	ROAD AND RAILWAY
- - - - -	TRACK

THE ROUTE

narrow ridge of high ground which gives splendid views along the Llanthony and Grwyne Fawr Valleys. The Dial Garreg or stone of revenge commemorates the murder hereabouts of Richard de Clare in the 12th Century.

Beyond Dial Garreg the mountain road follows the hillside above Grwyne Fawr passing a Forestry Commission plantation on the left. Immediately in front is Bal Mawr (1991 ft) and the Ffwddog ridge. The path to Llanthony diverges to the right, was used by the Blaen-y-cwm navvies on their way to the Half Moon Inn. The descent of Cwm Bwchel to Llanthony is very rewarding. Continuing along the mountain road (also the navvy route at this point), the Ffwddog ridge rises to 2228 ft. on the right and the peaks of the Gader ridge can be seen on the left. In front, the course of the mountain road is clear until it reaches the next conifer encroachment some two miles ahead. Before reaching this plantation use the gate above Cefn Coed Ewyas and follow the stream past the ruined building from which a good path descends to Blaen-y-cwm house and the village site.

Lower Cwmyoy to Fforest. The Route now traverses the ravine between the Bryn Arw and Twyn-y-Gaer hills. The site of P.P. No. 16 is below Cwm Cottage which is followed by the little hamlet of Cwm Coed-y-Cerrig. For a while the Board had a siding and a sawmill here. Several old paths converge at this spot and mark the boundaries of four parishes, Crucorney, Ffwddog, Llantilio Pertholey and Lower Cwmyoy. For a short distance the route twists over the course of an old track, goes through P.P. No. 15 and on to the new cut for a straight half mile through the marsh. P.P. No. 14 is visible in the brushwood on the right. On this section some of the metal railing that protected the railway can be seen. The Route emerges from the ravine and at the next bend Partrishow Hill comes into view with Gelli Welltog farm high up on its slope. To the left is the Sugar Loaf mountain, Mynydd Pen-y-Fal in Welsh, 1,955 ft. above sea level. In clear weather the summit is visible but the Fal is "a mountain on whose barren breast the labouring clouds do often rest". Grinding round the sharp bend from which the DUKINFIELD was derailed in 1913 the train arrived at Pont Esgob depot. The word means the Bishop's Bridge. Spread out on the hillside is the village of Fforest Coalpit, the little metropolis for the Grwyne Fawr Valley. The reference is to one-time charcoal burning, not coal mining. The whitewashed building is the Calvinistic Methodist Church. At first Lady Huntingdon supplied preachers from her college near Talgarth and Welsh services continued until 1905. Nearby Chapel farm was bequeathed to the cause by a saintly old farmer who lived until he was 102. "Uncle Tom" Pembridge used to be the driving force at the Sunday School. He worked for the contractor in Messam's day, served the Water Board, sang in the male voice choir at Blaen-y-cwm and farmed at Fforest until his death in January 1974. The Day School building is now a Mountain Centre. Following the line of the road down the hillside, it passes the Globe Inn building now a dwelling house. Here the navvies drank whisky, neat, at 4s. 6d. a bottle. The pub had never seen such days and never did so again. The extension railway and the motors took people into town and the Globe closed in 1915. At the bottom of the hill two sets of forge buildings remain but the clink of the hammer on the anvil has not been heard for many years. Nearer the Route is Pontyspig farm. The building looks old enough to be Elizabethan.

The Lewis's farm is here and Mrs. Lewis was formerly a Miss Morgan of Blaen-y-cwm House. Beside the stream and the old pack horse bridge is the miller's cottage, the corn mill is on the other side of the stream and both buildings are now dwelling houses. Miller Dick Duggan ground oats and barley for cattle fodder, also wheat for bread. Dick was a "regular" at the Globe, so regular in fact that he often spent a week or a fortnight at the pub. Meanwhile work at the mill piled up. It was not until the noise of the machinery could be heard again that villagers knew Dick was back at work. Miller Duggan left the corn mill about 1908. He was succeeded by Mr. Prosser, but farmer Philip Parsons was there before the war. Thomas joined his father in 1913 and brother Charles came to the mill in 1917. During the war the place was a hive of activity. Regular grinding ceased in 1922 though the machinery was not removed until 1962. At Pont Esgob the lanes from Abergavenny and Crickhowell converge to form one track up the Ffwddog, past the New Inn and on to the mountain road. When the Board opened their Route the intersection became "Five-ways" to the eternal mystification of the tourist who is usually too engrossed in trying to discover where he wants to go to notice where he actually is. This is a pity because Fforest has a charm of its own. Until the First World War period the little community was practically self-supporting.

Pont Esgob was the first turn-out or loop where the trains could pass. There was also a siding here. In the roadway three manhole covers indicate that the conduit is now below the route. One stormy winter night Mr. Bill Jackson of Abergavenny went to Pont Esgob to join a concert party travelling from Llanfihangel to Blaen-y-cwm by train. After waiting for over an hour a light engine came down the valley and the driver told him that the other one had broken down and that he had come from Blaen-y-cwm to *"do his best"*. He drove off into the night. Bill spent another hour at Pont Esgob before the train returned from Llanfihangel. The engine was one of the large Manning Wardles together with the Glass Coach. The rain soon turned to snow but they battled on, reached the Village, visited the canteen, gave the concert and arrived back at Pont Esgob at 2.30 a.m. Bill said *"goodnight"* to the driver who once more set off for Llanfihangel, saying he *"hoped to be back at Blaen-y-cwm in time for work"*.

Fforest (Pont Esgob) to Blaen-y-cwm (6 miles). A small bridge carries the Route over the river Grwyne, crossed here for the first time, and into the hills.

The first incline begins beyond the corn mill, passes over the dried up millrace and the site of P.P. No. 13 before reaching a summit at Gwern-y-Bustach. Just before the mill race the Board laid down a siding in order to reach the timber on the far side of the stream. The latter was crossed by means of wood baulks with rails laid on them. In this way locomotives went across the stream to reach the sawmill. The train climbed at 1 in 18, 1 in 14 and 1 in 13 and the right hand embankment is now strengthened by lengths of rail driven into the ground. Strong retaining walls had to be built by the contractor at Gwern-y-busbach, where there are fine views of the surrounding hills. The Route is now in the heart of Grwyne Fawr territory, once described as "a very great area which, until a few years ago lay open and common to a great part of the adjoining country. Tenants and inhabitants of Talgarth, Crickhowell,

Llanbedr and other villages had free common time out of mind, without paying pannage or rent'' (Exchequer Proceedings 1605).

Beyond the summit is a short, steep, descent to the Nant-Mair stream at 1 in 19. Even on this gradient a cutting and embankment were necessary, the latter has the stream culvert below. The wall is now badly cracked and large trees grow out of it. On the right a sleeper gatepost is complete with ''dog'' clips and bolts. At the bottom of the incline a lane ascends to Tyn-y-Llwyn Manor farm and Partrishow Church, the latter always hidden in the trees. The Church is famous for its rood screen, Saxon font and Anchorite's cell. The farm building is again basically Tudor, it was once the home of the Herberts and has their crest. Below a chimney is the date 1649. The farmer, Mr. Leonard Parker, is one of Inspector Parker's sons. To the left there is a glimpse of Partrishow Hill and Crug Mawr mountain. Beyond P.P. No. 12 is the ruin of Ty'n-y-Pant farm and a stream runs below the road. The trains stopped here for the locomotives to take water and the tank is preserved at Cwm Coed-y-Cerrig.

Descending towards the stream the Baptist Chapel is visible through the trees on the right. Known as the Tabernacle, or the 'Tab', it was built in 1837. The access road and bridge were built after the Board had opened their reservoir. At this point the retaining wall is about fifty feet above the river and the Route climbs gently towards P.P. No. 11. On the right is Y Coed farm, on the left the site of the oakwood purchased by the Board to make sleepers. The sawmill here was driven from the flywheel of a traction engine. Farmer Thomas remembers the trains and his brother-in-law was once the Blaen-y-cwm postman, footing it over the mountain with his sack of mail. Y Coed farmhouse is a rare example of the Welsh long house with an ancient cruck beam still visible. Two more farms can be seen across the valley but beyond this point farms give way to Forestry Commission plantations.

The Route is again cut out of the hillside with a long section of retaining wall on the right. The site of P.P. No. 10 is still visible and at Neuadd Wen Barn the valley opens out to give a skyline view of the Ffwddog Ridge above Coed Dias wood. Mr. Baker-Gabb's house is on the right and the contractor built the access road and bridge. This house was built near the end of the last century on the site of an existing farm building. Before the Board's road was made it could only be reached from the Llanthony Valley, by foot, or on horseback. At this point the Route enters what the Forestry Commission describe as the Mynydd Du or Black Mountain Forest. To the left closely planted conifers erode and spoil the ground. To the right are pasture, house and ridge. It is a stark contrast. Hereabouts was turnout No. 2, the last passing place before Blaen-y-cwm, followed by rock cutting. Here the Route is just above river level with a wall on each side, the width being approximately thirteen feet. As a minimum of eight feet was required for the train the passing places were very useful. The site of No. 9 is obscured. The footbridge here is called Pont Cadwgan and up in the trees can be seen the former Cadwgan Farmhouse. P.P. No. 8 was nearby. At this point the Route cuts into the hillside and P.P. No. 7 was near the second picnic site which serves as the entrance to the forest walk.

The Route next curves away from the river, climbing up the mountainside at

Wall Hill, over a switchback summit and down a straight descent to P.P. No. 6. Here there is a sharp right-hand bend passing a Forestry Commission house. The spot is called Ty-Hir and marks the termination of the track lifting in 1917. Beyond Ty-Hir there is another climb and descent to river level P.P. No. 5, followed by yet a further climb giving a fine view of the Ffwddog ridge. "Jack catches" were fitted on the inclines, being the local term for catch points to throw off runaway wagons. P.P. No. 4 was at Nant-y-Bedd near the post-box where there is another Forestry house and depot. The Route curves around the hillside and two more Forestry houses come into view at Ty-isaf. P.P. No. 3 was opposite the second house. Still climbing, the access to Cae Capel sheepfold is Underwood's work and then comes the final descent to P.P. No. 2 and the bridge across the stream leading to Blaen-y-cwm House. The end of a length of rail protrudes from the wall of the house, used for lifting materials into a small workshop by means of block and tackle. A final ascent at 1 in 39 takes the Route up to the site of the village. The steps that led down to the footbridge and across the river to give access to the school buildings remain, also the column that supported the bridge.

Blaen-y-cwm to the Reservoir (two miles). At the Village, the track layout consisted of a loop and siding into the locomotive shed. The loop line was used for all through traffic, the main line was used to stable stock for the mail trains. At the Village, the Route divided into two. Work No. 7, the road, is cut into the mountainside and climbs to the reservoir. The unmetalled surface has the pipeline below ground until it reaches 1,590 ft. when it diverges to the left in order to reach the base of the reservoir. The road continues to the termination of the works just beyond the catchment area where it reverts to a rough track over the mountain and down to Llanelieu Common. P.P. No. 1 was just beyond the Village on this hillside section.

The route to the reservoir follows the course of the stream. The road terminated at the brick bungalow beyond which the railway crossed the Grwyne for the third time. Before reaching the site of the railway works the small concrete bridge can be noted on the right. This took the railway to the top of the reservoir in 1927, after the tunnel had been filled in.

Near the reservoir wall, a number of buildings are visible to the right of the Route, including the recorder hut, the screen chamber or filter, the chlorination plant and meter house. The corrugated iron building on the left is the former works store. By rail the Quarry was 11¾ miles from Llanfihangel Yard. Flooding has not entirely obscured the Quarry and part of the face is always visible. Before reaching the boundary fence Underwood's small dam and meter house of 1915 can be seen. Beyond is the *"great parcel of land called Grwyne Fawr, being part of a great waste in the parish of Talgarth and in the lordship manor or territory of Dinas"* (Exchequer Proceedings 1610).

ii THE MAIN

The large output of modern reservoirs makes the A & DWB's two million gallons a day seem insignificant. Its value lies in being a gravity feed which does not require pumping and is cheap to operate. The trouble spot remains where it always has been, in Coity tunnel.

Beyond Pont Esgob the main diverges left through the fields to pass Fforest Mountain Centre, and on to the east side of the Sugar Loaf Mountain. The course around the mountainside can be followed by the footpath from Fforest Post Office and several manhole covers are lettered "Frederick Bird & Co., A. & DWB Engineers London". The pipe and track rise quickly to a height of 1350 ft. before beginning the long descent to the Usk. After crossing the Deri mountain path the main passes through a wood side above the Cibbi Valley with the Cibbi Springs high on the mountainside. This stream is crossed "by a trivial piece of engineering" and the pipe descends on the edge of Park Wood to Porth-y-Parc Farm (836 ft.) and the nearby car park where the metalled road is reached.

Near Abergavenny is the Town's small Llwyn Ddu Reservoir built in 1913 to store Cibbi Water. This reservoir is adjacent to the Abertillery pipe but the two systems remained separate until the drought of 1976 after which the Gwent Water Authority decided to let "bygones be bygones" and put in a connecting valve. At this point the pressure in the Abertillery pipe is 500 lb. p.s.i.

The route then traverses the suburbs of Abergavenny and at Cherry Orchard the main crosses the A.40 and Llanwenarth roads before going under the Usk at 150 ft. above sea level. The fall from the mountainside is 1200 ft. and here the pipe pressure is 630 lb. p.s.i.

Beyond the river is Cadfor Farm, the A.465(M) and the Cadfor Pumping Station. The Abertillery pipe had to be lowered when the A.465 was built and a black and white post on the river side of the road locates the point of crossing . Here the A. & D.W.B. main also crosses the Talybont to Newport pipe and after the drought a pumping station was built at Cadfor so that when necessary up to three-quarters of a million gallons a day can be fed into the Abertillery main.

At the road junction the pipe is laid below the B.4246 Blaenavon road until this turns left above the canal and the pipe route follows the road to Glaslin and up the side of the Clydach gorge. At Cwm Llanwenarth Bailey's tramroad bridge is used to cross the stream beyond which the pipe crosses several fields before regaining the lane at Shop Newydd.

A rough track lifts the pipe to the road which skirts Gilwern Hill and up to a height of 1000 ft. before a steep descent and ascent is necessary to reach the side of Llanelly Hill, then up to Waun Wen and the B.4248 Brynmawr to Blaenavon road. The main follows this road as far as the Whistle Inn where it turns right and climbs to Coity tunnel.

Coity is a great lump rising to 1905 ft above sea level and blocking the way from the Eastern to the Western Valleys. It is also a much troubled mountain, sombre, and at times hideous. For a century or more before our period, men had bored and burrowed into it for ore and coal, then they bombarded the tops with heavy machinery, seeking open cast coal. No building is secure on Coity Mountain; it subsides. Near to the tunnel mouth is the site of the Milfraen Colliery sunk in the 1840's and closed in 1929 after an underground

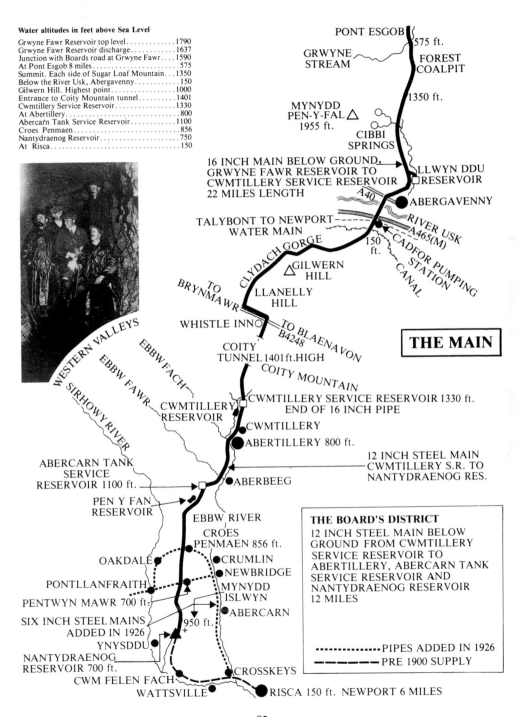

Water altitudes in feet above Sea Level

Grwyne Fawr Reservoir top level............1790
Grwyne Fawr Reservoir discharge...........1637
Junction with Boards road at Grwyne Fawr....1590
At Pont Esgob 8 miles......................575
Summit. Each side of Sugar Loaf Mountain...1350
Below the River Usk, Abergavenny...........150
Gilwern Hill. Highest point................1000
Entrance to Coity Mountain tunnel.........1401
Cwmtillery Service Reservoir...............1330
At Abertillery.............................800
Abercarn Tank Service Reservoir...........1100
Croes Penmaen..............................856
Nantydraenog Reservoir.....................750
At Risca...................................150

PONT ESGOB

575 ft.

GRWYNE
STREAM

FOREST
COALPIT

1350 ft.

MYNYDD
PEN-Y-FAL △
1955 ft.

CIBBI
SPRINGS

16 INCH MAIN BELOW GROUND,
GRWYNE FAWR RESERVOIR TO
CWMTILLERY SERVICE RESERVOIR
22 MILES LENGTH

LLWYN DDU
RESERVOIR

A40

ABERGAVENNY

TALYBONT TO NEWPORT
WATER MAIN

RIVER USK
A465(M)

CADFOR PUMPING STATION

150 ft.

CLYDACH GORGE

CANAL

TO
BRYNMAWR

GILWERN
HILL △

LLANELLY
HILL

WHISTLE INN

TO BLAENAVON
B4248

COITY
TUNNEL 1401 ft. HIGH

COITY MOUNTAIN

THE MAIN

WESTERN VALLEYS

EBBW FACH

EBBW FAWR

SIRHOWY RIVER

CWMTILLERY
RESERVOIR

CWMTILLERY SERVICE RESERVOIR 1330 ft.
END OF 16 INCH PIPE

CWMTILLERY

ABERTILLERY 800 ft.

12 INCH STEEL MAIN
CWMTILLERY S.R. TO
NANTYDRAENOG RES.

ABERCARN TANK
SERVICE
RESERVOIR 1100 ft.

ABERBEEG

PEN Y FAN
RESERVOIR

EBBW RIVER

CROES
PENMAEN 856 ft.

OAKDALE

CRUMLIN

NEWBRIDGE

PONTLLANFRAITH

MYNYDD
ISLWYN

PENTWYN MAWR 700 ft.

ABERCARN

SIX INCH STEEL MAINS
ADDED IN 1926

950 ft.

YNYSDDU

NANTYDRAENOG
RESERVOIR 700 ft.

CWM FELEN FACH

CROSSKEYS

WATTSVILLE

RISCA 150 ft. NEWPORT 6 MILES

THE BOARD'S DISTRICT

12 INCH STEEL MAIN BELOW
GROUND FROM CWMTILLERY
SERVICE RESERVOIR TO
ABERTILLERY, ABERCARN TANK
SERVICE RESERVOIR AND
NANTYDRAENOG RESERVOIR
12 MILES

·············· PIPES ADDED IN 1926
———————— PRE 1900 SUPPLY

93

explosion killed nine men. Today the pipe tunnel still sinks, and shakes while successive generations of engineers struggle with a problem that will not go away. Heavy repairs were carried out in 1957 when the tunnel was lined with steel colliery arches set in concrete. At this time the portals were also concrete faced and incised 'A & DWB', a notice that cannot be easily obliterated. In 1983 £60,000 was spent on tunnel repairs which should see the century out. Time will tell. Despite all the problems, including the rock fault, Coity tunnel is finely poised entering the mountain at 1401 ft above sea level and some twenty miles from the impounding source. If the tunnel were a few feet higher that water would not flow; if it was lower, the bore would have to be longer.

Beyond the tunnel mouth the main is in the Valley of Tillery stream and the 16 inch main terminates at the 2 million gallon Cwmtillery Service Reservoir 22 miles from Grwyne Fawr Reservoir. Nearby is the older Cwmtillery Reservoir which impounds the stream water only and both pipes use the modern Cwmtillery Treatment Works.

Below Cwmtillery Service Reservoir the 12 inch steel main follows the railway, then travels beneath the Tillery East Bank road to Cwmtillery and Abertillery where it crosses the valley to use the Ebbw West Bank road to Aberbeeg.

Beyond Aberbeeg the main climbs the side of Mynydd Pen-y-Fal to reach the 2 million gallon circular service reservoir called Abercarn Tank. From this point the route is south past the Pen-y-fan reservoir, built to supply the Crumlin Canal, then to Croes Penmaen, Pentwyn Mawr and the Blacksmiths Arms near Mynyddislwyn Church. Here the pipe crosses several fields to augment Nantydraenog Reservoir, 33 miles from Grwyne Fawr Reservoir.

This reservoir was built about 1900 by the former Western Valleys Gas and Water Board without an act of Parliament or official authority. The local need for a domestic water supply was acute and was met by a local agreement, sealed by a handshake. In this way the colliery villages and Risca obtained their water. However, when the Board decided to terminate their pipe main at Nantydraenog to augment the supply, they ran into problems because, legally, there was no such reservoir. Legal hands scratched wise legal heads and with great wisdom they concluded. "It was deemed that consent to construct HAD been given".

In 1926 the four U.D.C.s relinquished responsibility for supplying their Districts and the work was taken over by the A. & D.W.B. The Board added six inch steel mains from Croespenmaen to Oakdale and Pontllanfraith, also to Crumlin, Newbridge, Abercarn and Crosskeys, with an augmented supply from Pentwyn Mawr. This completed the Western Valleys water circuit and with the opening of the Grwyne Fawr reservoir gave an adequate water supply to the District.

As a piece of old time Water Works engineering the scheme was well thought out and remains effective today. The exception being Nantydraenog reservoir which was rendered superfluous in 1979 following developments at Llandegfed.

Mynyddislwyn gives its name to the Parliamentary Borough of which Neil Kinnock is currently MP. St. Tudur's Church has a 6th century dedication and is a 14th or 15th century building. The first tracks kept to the high ground and today St. Tudur's is still a lofty mountain sentinel in a beautiful setting. Here converge several routes from the Sirhowy Valley to 'service' two pubs and the burial ground.

St. Tudur's churchyard is an excellent place in which to conclude the story of the 'Board'. Coffins used to be carried up the mountain from the Sirhowy valley by two teams of bearers (it's a long pull) and the custom was to stop at The Nailers Inn for a drink and to change teams. The corpse was left outside the pub while the bearers met inside, but a new landlord did not like this custom and, meeting it for the first time, promptly had the coffin moved out of sight. Meanwhile both teams of bearers went on refreshing themselves inside. This led to terrible confusion because they emerged separately and saw the coffin 'gone'. Each thought the other team had done the bearing. The relief team was particularly agitated, believing that the first team would claim all the fee money. Both teams met at the churchyard where the vicar and funeral party were waiting. The confused and excited Welshmen tried to explain the incident, but all the clergyman wanted was the COFFIN. Where was THAT? Back they trooped to find it and staggered up the hill again making what speed they could, but they were very late indeed. To cap it all, when the coffin was finally lowered into the ground an onlooker was heard to say, "There goes poor old Harry 'Man', but he won't go any further", and neither did the main, which had reached its destination, namely (in the words of Francis Jupp) the Nantydraenog reservoir BELOW Mynyddislwyn Church'. Terminus ad quem.

iii LOCOMOTIVES WORKING ON THE ABERTILLERY & DISTRICT WATER BOARD RAILWAY

Name	Type	Maker	No.	Date Built	Date on Site	Date to A&DWB		Date of Disposal
DUKINFIELD	0-6-OST	Bagnall	1669	1902	4/1913	12/1916	Sold	6/1928
ANITA	0-4-OST	Manning Wardle	1630	1904	4/1913	12/1916	Sold	6/1928
BRIGG	0-4-OST	Hudswell Clarke	504	1898		7/1919	Sold	5/1928
ABERTILLERY No. 1	0-6-OST	Manning Wardle	1985	1920		4/1920	Sold	12/1928
ABERTILLERY No. 2	0-6-OST	Manning Wardle	1986	1920		5/1920	Sold	12/1928
STANLEY	0-4-OST	Black Hawthorn	872	1880		6/1925	Sold	12/1928
MOUNTAIN ASH	0-4-OST	Bagnall	1682	1902		6/1925	Sold	12/1928

DUKINFIELD. New to Enoch Tempest for the Halifax Corporation Waterworks at Walshaw Dean. The locomotive was in the hands of William Underwood & Brother of Dukinfield by May 1912, hence the name, and it was used by him on the construction of the Penderyn Waterworks, Glamorgan. From Penderyn it is understood to have been transported by road to Lower Cwmyoy. Had a round top saddle tank with domed boiler, 9" x 14" cylinders and 2' 3" wheels. Sold by the Board to Messrs. Lehane Mackenzie & Shand Ltd. for £125 and used by them on the Halifax Corporation Gorple Reservoir construction where it was named BURTON. Photographed at Lehane Mackenzie & Shand's yard, Darley Dale, Derbyshire in November 1937. No further record.

ANITA. Special design, i.e., it was not a Manning Wardle standard class engine. Went new to Elliots Metal Co. Ltd. at Burry Port, Carmarthenshire.

Sold in 1913 to William Underwood & Bro. by C.D. Phillips (dealer) of Newport, Mon., for £220. Fitted with a square saddle tank and domeless boiler working at 140 lb. per square inch. 9½" by 14" cylinders, and 2' 4" wheels. Wheel base 4' 0", heating surface 232 square feet, tank capacity 250 gallons. A neat looking engine due to the fact that it was the only one fitted with spring buffers instead of wooden blocks. Capable of hauling 8 or 9 tons of cement to the reservoir site. The Board sold ANITA for £125 to Lehane Mackenzie & Shand Ltd. who used it on the Gorple reservoir construction and at Fernilee reservoir built for Stockport Corporation. The name was changed to DERBY and the locomotive was photographed in 1938 at Darley Dale. The next owner was Pauling & Co. Ltd. who are understood to have used DERBY on wartime contracts. The locomotive was seen at their Danygraig Yard, Swansea, in 1948 and is believed to have been cut up there about 1950.

BRIGG. New to Newcastle & Gateshead Water Co., Catcleugh reservoir construction in Northumberland until about 1906. Later it was used by H. Arnold & Son Ltd. on the Leighton reservoir construction for Leeds Corporation and by the Ministry of Munitions. Purchased by the A&DWB in July 1919 and sold by the Board to Lehane Mackenzie & Shand Ltd. for £200. Thence to Gorple reservoir (above) where it was renamed HESWALL and also used at Fernilee. Last reported at the L.M. & S. Yard at Matlock in 1948. Domeless boiler, 9" x 15" cylinders and 2' 3" wheels.

ABERTILLERY No. 1 and ABERTILLERY No. 2. Both built for the Board's railway in 1920. Fine locomotives with fluted chimneys and spark arresters, spacious cabs, acetylene headlamps, rail washers and lifting jacks. The usual Manning Wardle style square saddle tank was fitted. Domeless boilers made of best mild steel plates with copper fireboxes and brass tubes. Nameplates also cast in brass with letters 3½" and 2½" high (ANITA and STANLEY also had cast nameplates, BRIGG, DUKINFIELD and MOUNTAIN ASH had the names painted on the tank sides). These locomotives were also fitted with both steam and hand brakes. Three engines of a generally similar design had been supplied by Manning Wardle to the Kettering Iron & Coal Co. Ltd., Northants between 1889 and 1906. The last (M.W. 1675 of 1906) being preserved at Kettering. A comparative dimension table is supplied for Kettering Furnaces No. 8 (M.W. 1675) and A&DWB Nos. 1 and 2 (M.W. 1985/86).

	M.W. 1675	M.W. 1985/6
Gauge	3' 0"	3' 0"
Cylinders	11½" x 17"	11" x 17"
Wheels	2'9"	2'6"
Wheelbase	7'9"	7'2"
Boiler pressure	140 p.s.i.	160 p.s.i.
Heating surface	350 sq. ft.	385 sq. ft.
Tubes	56 x 2" dia.	60 x 2" dia.
Grate area	5 sq. ft.	6¼ sq. ft.
Tank capacity	400 gallons	450 gallons

Apart from the ½" diameter increase in cylinder size it is interesting to observe that the Board's locomotives were larger than the Kettering locomotives in all but two dimensions. Surprisingly, they had smaller diameter wheels and a shorter wheelbase. The steep gradients and sharp curves on the Route made this necessary but the tremendous overhang at each end contributed to the original unsteadiness. At the end of 1928 Joseph Pugsley & Sons of Bristol purchased both locomotives, together with STANLEY, MOUNTAIN ASH and other items for £3,300. 1985 and 1986 remained at Crucorney until February 1929 and were under repair at the Avonside Engine Works, Bristol in September 1929 before being shipped out to Singapore. Both locomotives were sent to the South Dam of the Pontian Kechil Reservoir (now the Farrer Reservoir) in the Malayan hills where the Singapore Water Works was under construction. A photograph reveals that one engine was renamed 'Griffith Jones'. The Farrer Reservoir was completed in 1931 and the following year the Municipality of Singapore ordered two new boilers from the English firm of Kitson & Co. Both locomotives were then sent to Hong Kong where they were last noted in 1934.

STANLEY. History incomplete. Went new to Heywood Corporation, Lancashire, sold by them in July 1890. Later obtained by William Underwood & Bro. and used on the Penderyn reservoir site as from 1912. 8″ x 14″ cylinders, 2′ 4″ wheels. Purchased by the Board in June 1925 from A.R. Adams & Son of Newport, Mon. and sold to Joseph Pugsley & Sons in December 1928.

MOUNTAIN ASH. New to Enoch Tempest for the construction of the Walshaw Dean Reservoir, near Halifax, Yorkshire. Named GEORGE at this time. Later to William Underwood & Bro. and used at Penderyn where it was photographed as the MOUNTAIN ASH. Sold in December 1924 and purchased by the Board in June 1925 together with STANLEY for £775. Sold to Joseph Pugsley & Sons in December 1928 who resold it to the County Borough of Derby where it was used on the Derby Riverlands Scheme between Borrowash and Derby. Renamed RIVERLANDS DORA and photographed. In 1934 sold to H. Potter & Co., dealers, of Nottingham. 9″ x 14″ cylinders, 2′ 3½″ wheels. It was advertised for sale by W. Twigg of Matlock, Derbyshire in 1935 and in 1936.

Locomotive Depots. The A&DWB Railway had four locomotive depots. Lower Cwmyoy was opened in 1913 and closed in 1919 when it was replaced by the shed at Crucorney from 1919 to 1928. Blaen-y-cwm shed was opened in 1913, enlarged in 1920 and closed in 1928. Grwyne Fawr Works Shed and repair shop was opened in 1921, enlarged in 1923 and closed in 1928.

iv THE GLASS COACH & THE AMBULANCE

Mr. J.H.L. Bate, Engineer to the Tal-y-llyn Railway says that the glass coach *"was built by Kerr Short & Co. about 1900, probably for a water works construction job and was most likely disused after 1914"*. The coach was acquired by the Board early in 1920, without glass and with the end windows boarded up. It was repaired and reglazed at Grwyne Fawr Works. In 1928 the Board sold the glass coach to Messrs. Lehane McKenzie and Shand for £10 and it went to the Halifax Corporation Gorple reservoir construction. This was followed by a long spell with Boden's Stone Co. Ltd. at Stanton-in-the-Peak, Derbyshire, where the coach was used as a quarry stores. In 1957 it was acquired by the Tal-y-llyn Railway Preservation Society where it was known as the Stanton coach. The superstructure was decayed but the underframe and bogies were incorporated with a certain amount of new material and a new body to become the Tal-y-llyn Railway carriage No. 16. At Towyn the vehicle is still referred to as the Stanton coach, though the Abertillery Saloon would be better!

As received at Towyn the vehicle was 20 ft. long, 6′6″ wide and 8′6″ high. The respective dimensions are now 23 ft. 6 inches, 5 ft. 8 inches and 8ft. 3 inches. Much of the underframe and both bogies are entirely original. The axles were simply cut back and re-machined to reduce the gauge from 3′0″ to 2′3″ and the frame members were also cut back by 9 inches. The original draw hooks are still in use.

Inspection party and the Glass Coach, Locomotive Anita.

The Board repaired and rebuilt wagons left behind by the contractor. They did not use bogie wagons and fitted their vehicles with small diameter wheels. Rebuilding feats included shortening some 7 ft. axles to fit the 3ft. gauge railway and fitting the wheels by means of a press. In 1920 some new wagons were built at Llanfihangel where the first coach was also built in 1922. In May 1924 the wagon works was moved to Grwyne Fawr where foreman joiner Eddie Hawkins built some more coaches using the chassis and wheels "from Messam's time". The only surviving pieces of rolling stock are a chassis with wheels and a body-cum-chassis without wheels, both preserved at Pen-y-clawdd Court farm. The latter was the ambulance and probably the coach built in 1922. Kept at Blaen-y-cwm it was quite a sophisticated vehicle used only in cases of emergency. The body is 10′ long by 6′6″ wide and the centre height from floor to roof is 6′6″. The ambulance has four glazed windows opened by lowering the straps in the former main line style. Sliding doors were fitted at one end and there are sliding ventilators on each side of the vehicle. Inside there are six tip-up seats clipped to the sides when not in use. The stretcher was passed through a flap door at the end of the coach and was slung from the roof by means of four steel hooks and pins which are still in position.

In the nearby field the chassis has spoked wheels 15" diameter and 4" wide, on a wheel base of 4'9". The gauge is 3 ft. Two main timber bearers each 6" by 6" and 12' long support seven transverse timbers. The centre coupling chain is attached to each of the main timbers as are the two side safety chains. They remain in position on both vehicles. In addition to the glass coach and the ambulance there were finally about fifteen 4 wheel coaches, all of which were used on the workmen's mails to and from the dam.

v ROAD v RAIL IN 1910

Before the first World War no experienced contractor would have contemplated a major construction such as the A. & D.W.B. job without laying down a narrow gauge access railway. However, the Board obtained power for a new road up the valley, and which in 1910 was revolutionary. Why did they do it? Engineer Latham must have known that the steep gradients would be difficult to operate with traction engines and trailer(s). Also that the only alternative was the steam lorry which had a very heavy axle load. (Petrol and diesel lorries belonged to the future).

A careful reading of the Minutes of the A. & D.W.B. Bill as recorded by the House of Lords' Select Committee in March and June 1910 seems to supply the answer to the question, 'Why a road?'. The reason was vested interests.

On page 3 we read, *"Your Grace will see that a road is necessary for the purpose of the reservoir and also desirable in the interests of Lord Glanusk's property"*. Again later, *"We have arranged with Lord Glanusk and other landowners through whose property the main and road passes"* etc. The landowners were also motorcar owners but they had no means of driving to their farms, and shooting sites in Grwyne Fawr. If land was acquired from them at a nominal sum (stated), then the road was a 'perk'. The Board took a calculated risk (which didn't come off), but it did give the landowners their new road.

In 1918 Jupp reported to his Board, *"It will be remembered that the Scheme as originally laid out did not provide for any railway up the Grwyne Fawr Valley. It was proposed that materials should be hauled to the Dam by road. This arrangement was carried out for a time but Underwoods soon found out(!) that the new road with its steep gradients would not stand the heavy traffic, and in November 1912 they approached the Board on the subject of putting down a light railway along the new road. Ultimately the Board agreed to advance them £5000 of the retention money on the understanding that the railway would be put down at the contractor's expense — and this was done. The contractor recognised the need to extend the railway across the fields from Lower Cwmyoy but failed to come to terms with the landowners"*.

All of which reveals the astuteness of the Board's professional men and the power of the vested interests who needed a road up their valley but not a railway across their fields! The statement about the new road being "too steep" is significant too!

As it is frequently claimed that the original intention was to work the traffic by rail, a summary of the evidence against this is included:

1. The House of Lords Minutes refer to the new road.

2. The 1910 Act authorised a road.

3. Mr. Baker-Gabb, a local landowner, gives an enthusiastic description of the new road in his "Hills and Vales of the Black Mountains", published in 1913.

4. The officials and guests who took part in the ceremony of cutting the first sod of the Dam foundation in October 1912 all travelled up the valley by road.

5. Underwood's reminder to the Board in 1915, to the effect that initial delays were due to the unsuitability of their road, which he had re-surfaced at his own cost.

6. The Minute books for 1916, 1917, 1918 and 1919 refer to the fact that in the beginning no powers for a railway were sought.

7. This is confirmed by newspaper reports of 1912 and 1921.

vi THE 1845 RAILWAY CLAUSES CONSOLIDATION ACT

The following extract is taken from the Board's Act of 1910. As recorded it is incomprehensible but, to the Engineer and Contractor, it proved to be invaluable.

"With respect to the temporary occupation of lands near the railway during the construction thereof and in the application of that Act to this Act the term railways shall mean reservoirs roads railways and so much of the aqueducts conduits or lines of pipes as will not be constructed in a highway and the works immediately connected therewith by this Act authorised and the expression centre of railway shall respectively mean the boundaries of the reservoirs and the centres of the roads and railway and so much of the said aqueducts culverts or lines of pipes as aforesaid".

vii CHRONOLOGY

1906   First surveys carried out in Grwyne Fawr Valley.

1908   Monmouthshire County Council's Water Bill defeated in Parliament.

1909   Formation of A. & D.W.B.

1910   August 3rd. Act of Parliament to incorporate the Abertillery and District Water Board received Royal Assent.

1911	December 13th. Contract secured by William Underwood & Brother, Dukinfield, Cheshire.
1912	October 16th. Completion of the new access road from Lower Cwmyoy to the catchment area. The cutting of the first sod at the reservoir site.
1913	Commencement of the navvy village at Blaen-y-cwm. September: Railway laid down on the Board's new road.
1914	July 8th. Second A. and D.W.B. Act of Parliament to authorise the Helyg reservoir.
1915	April 1st. Underwood completes the pipeline and the water is turned on. July: The Helyg reservoir scheme is abandoned. December 31st: Agreed to suspend all work for the duration of the war.
1916	December 1st: Contractor Underwood is released and the Board take over the work.
1917	The Ministry of Munitions requisition the railway for the War Department.
1919	The Board restart construction. May 20th: Third A. and D.W.B. Act of Parliament to authorise a ten year extension of time. June 25th: Extension railway opened to Llanfihangel Yard.
1920	The quarry at the northern extremity is brought into use.
1925	Over 400 people reported living at Blaen-y-cwm and 49 children attending the day school.
1926	The final cost of the scheme estimated at £1 million. July 8th: Fourth A. and D.W.B. Act of Parliament authorising a ten year extension of time for repayment of borrowed money.
1927	September: Extension of railway to reservoir top at approximately 1,800 feet above sea level.
1928	February 10th: Reservoir filling begins. March 28th: Official opening day. November 25th: High water level reached for the first time.
1929/30	Demolition of the village and removal of the railway completed.
1970	April 1st: A. and D.W.B. becomes a part of the new Gwent Water Board.
1973/74	The Water Act creating ten Regional Water Authorities in England and Wales and the formation of the Welsh Water Authority.

BIBLIOGRAPHY

BAKER-GABB, R.H.	Hills and Vales of the Black Mountains.
BALE, GILLIAN M.	Cultural Changes in the Taf Fechan Valley, Breconshire.
BOWTELL, H.	Reservoir Railways of Manchester & the Peak.
BRADLEY, A.G.	Highways and Byways in South Wales.
DAVIES, Ivor	Ignatius the Monk.
JASPER, J.W.G.	The Black Mountains, Settlement Patterns.
ODELL, Robin	Exhumation of a Murder.
WILLIAMS, J.G.	Abergavenny, Historical Notes.

ASHTON-UNDER-LYNE REPORTER, 1924

DAILY SKETCH, March 1928

MONMOUTHSHIRE EVENING POST. October 1912

SOUTH WALES ARGUS. Various Issues

THE ENGINEER. October 1927

THE WOOLHOPE CLUB. Transactions June 1925.

PARLIAMENTARY PLANS. A. & D.W.B. November 1909.

PARLIAMENTARY DEBATES. Minutes 1910 Lords and Commons

A. and D.W.B. Minute Books. 1910-30

A. and D.W.B. Act of Parliament 1910, (by courtesy of Mr. S. George.)

JUPP, J. FRANCIS, Chief Engineer A. and D.W.B. A short description of the Works, March 1928.

A. and D.W.B. Year Book 1925.

"There is no life without water. Water is a treasure indispensable to all human activity". (European Water Charter, May 1968).

ACKNOWLEDGMENTS

It is a great pleasure to acknowledge the vast amount of assistance willingly given by so many people. Dai Lewis of Lower Cwmyoy provided the initial inspiration and he passed me on to "Uncle" Tom Pembridge who in turn sent me to engine driver Bill Kirby of Abergavenny. Gradually the chain lengthened. Also at Abergavenny lived Bill Jackson and the late Fred Prosser. Bill wrote some fine letters. His reminiscences have been invaluable. John Beardsmore's interest brought me into contact with the Abergavenny Steam Society and Hugh Phillips.

At Crucorney Vicarage, Rev. Alex and Joan Davies' help was always in the "second mile" class and through them I met Mr. & Mrs. Baynton and Myrtle Parker. The late Mr. E. Knight introduced me to Farmer Tegwyn Davies at Pen-y-Clawdd. At Stanton Manor farm Mr. Bevan filled in some gaps and so to Fforest where Mrs. Price had a photograph of the village and Tom Pembridge was always a mine of information. At Pontyspig farm Mrs. Lewis, a daughter of Shepherd Lewis Morgan, introduced me to other members of the Morgan family. At Tyn-y-Llwyn farm Len Parker produced some more photographs and gave me the Derbyshire address of his elder brothers Bill and Tom. They grew up at Blaen-y-cwm and Bill has a detailed knowledge of the whole project, also a very good memory. At Blaen-y-cwm House Leo and Isabel McGraghan put their specialised knowledge of all things local and technical at my disposal. Nearer the reservoir Messrs. Holland and Morgan were always helpful. Then over the mountain to Talgarth where the late local historian Edith Davies introduced me to Mr. E. Speake whose father made the tramp to the Quarry. At Llanthony Ted Jasper produced the 1917 photograph at Llwyn Celyn together with his son's thesis on the settlement patterns for the area, gratefully used with Dad's permission. At Newport I was frequently indebted to Messrs. Stanley George, Percy Beard and F.W. Fox.

Further afield, Harry Parr, the late Selwyn Pearce-Higgins, Harold Bowtell and Bernard Roberts have rendered much assistance especially with the railway material. Also Frank Smith, John Townsend, Kenneth Plant, Bill Williams, R. Gabbott, R. Redman and Richard Evans. Mr. W.B. Underwood and Colin Coupe helped with the contractor biography. The photographic prints were produced by Mr. F.W. Shuttleworth.

The second edition has been enriched by valuable contributions from Eddy Hawkins, Roy Edge, Stanley Edge, Jenny Denham (nee Edge), Stanley Bailey, Arthur Ridout, Harry Bayliss (junior), Ronald Copleston, John Morgan, Arthur Llewellyn, Percival Pearson, Miss B.F. Jupp, Arthur Holland, Mrs. Elizabeth Holland, Isabel McGraghan, Mr. J.H.L. Bate, Bill Perrin (junior), Harold Butcher, Frank Wiseman and Bert Evans. In conclusion publication was made possible through the willing help of the Welsh Water Authority staff, also of Hannah Haynes and Gladys Liddell of Rochdale.